£3. 80

Solutions to Revised Higher Mathematics
1989 – 1994

by

B. Hastie

ISBN 0 7169 3197 4

© *B. Hastie, 1994.*

The solutions printed in this publication do not emanate
from the Scottish Examination Board. They reflect the
author's opinion as to what the solution should be.

ROBERT GIBSON · Publisher
17 Fitzroy Place, Glasgow, G3 7SF.

CONTENTS

1989 Paper   ....
1990 Paper   1
1991 Paper   3
1992 Paper   4
1993 Paper   5
1994 Paper   7
Graphic Calculators 8
Frequency Chart   8

1

$$\text{Gradient}_{QR} = \frac{2-1}{-6-2} = -\frac{1}{8} \qquad \left\{ \text{use } m_1 \times m_2 = -1 \right\}$$

$$\Rightarrow \text{gradient}_{\text{altitude}} = 8 \qquad \left\{ \text{use } y - b = m(x-a) \right\}$$

$$\text{Eqn}_{\text{altitude}} \text{ is } y - (-1) = 8(x - (-1))$$

$$\underline{y = 8x + 7}$$

2

$$f(x) = 2x^3 + 5x^2 - 4x - 3 \qquad \left\{ \begin{array}{l} \text{Use synthetic division} \\ \text{Try factors of 3} \end{array} \right\}$$

$$
\begin{array}{r|rrrr}
1 & 2 & 5 & -4 & -3 \\
  &   & 2 & 7 & 3 \\
\hline
-3 & 2 & 7 & 3 & 0 \\
   &   & -6 & -3 & \\
\hline
   & 2 & 1 & 0 &
\end{array}
$$

$\Rightarrow (x-1)$ is a factor

$\Rightarrow (x+3)$ is a factor

$2x+1$ is a factor

Hence $f(x) = \underline{(x+3)(2x+1)(x-1)}$

3

(a)

$$2\underline{p} - \underline{q} + \underline{r} = 2(3\underline{i} - 3\underline{j} + 2\underline{k}) - (4\underline{i} - \underline{j} + \underline{k}) + (4\underline{i} - 2\underline{j} + 3\underline{k})$$

$$= 6\underline{i} - 6\underline{j} + 4\underline{k} - 4\underline{i} + \underline{j} - \underline{k} + 4\underline{i} - 2\underline{j} + 3\underline{k}$$

$$= \underline{6\underline{i} - 7\underline{j} + 6\underline{k}}$$

(b)

$$|2\underline{p} - \underline{q} + \underline{r}| = \sqrt{(6^2 + (-7)^2 + 6^2)} = \sqrt{121} = \underline{\underline{11}}$$

4

Since PQRS is a parallelogram

Then $\overrightarrow{RS} = \overrightarrow{QP}$

$$\underline{s} - \underline{r} = \underline{p} - \underline{q}$$

$$\underline{s} = \underline{p} - \underline{q} + \underline{r}$$

$$\underline{s} = \begin{pmatrix} 1 \\ 3 \\ 3 \end{pmatrix} - \begin{pmatrix} 4 \\ -2 \\ -2 \end{pmatrix} + \begin{pmatrix} 3 \\ 1 \\ 1 \end{pmatrix} = \begin{pmatrix} 0 \\ 6 \\ 6 \end{pmatrix} \Rightarrow \text{S is the point :-}$$

$$\underline{(0, 6, 6)}$$

3

Q5

$$\int (2x^2 + 3)\, dx = \frac{2x^3}{3} + 3x + C$$

Q6

$$\vec{AB} = \underline{b} - \underline{a} = \begin{pmatrix} -6 \\ -8 \\ 2 \end{pmatrix} \implies AB^2 = 36 + 64 + 4 = 104$$

$$\vec{BC} = \underline{c} - \underline{b} = \begin{pmatrix} -6 \\ 4 \\ -2 \end{pmatrix} \implies BC^2 = 36 + 16 + 4 = 56$$

$$\vec{AC} = \underline{c} - \underline{a} = \begin{pmatrix} -12 \\ -4 \\ 0 \end{pmatrix} \implies AC^2 = 144 + 16 + 0 = 160$$

Since $AC^2 = AB^2 + BC^2$ Then $\underline{A\hat{B}C = 90°}$

(Converse of Pythagoras) $\left\{ \text{check } \vec{BA}.\vec{BC} = 0 \right\}$

Q7

$$2 \sin 3x° - 1 = 0 \qquad \left\{ 0 \leqslant x \leqslant 180 \implies 0 \leqslant 3x \leqslant 540 \right\}$$
$$2 \sin 3x° = 1$$
$$\sin 3x° = \tfrac{1}{2}$$
$$3x = 30, 150, 390, 510$$
$$x = \underline{10, 50, 130, 170}$$

Q8

$$x^2 + 6x + 11 = x^2 + 6x + 9 - 9 + 11 \qquad \{ \text{complete the square} \}$$
$$= x^2 + 6x + 9 + 2$$
$$= \underline{(x+3)^2 + 2} \qquad \{ \text{Min. TP at } (-3, 2) \}$$

Max. Value of $\dfrac{1}{x^2+6x+11} = \dfrac{1}{\text{min. Value of } x^2+6x+11}$

$$= \underline{\underline{\tfrac{1}{2}}}$$

Q9

$$\underline{a} \cdot (\underline{a} + \underline{b} + \underline{c}) = \underline{a}.\underline{a} + \underline{a}.\underline{b} + \underline{a}.\underline{c} \qquad \left\{ \begin{array}{l} \text{Multiply out} \\ \text{or} \\ \text{use } \underline{b} = \underline{a} + \underline{c} \end{array} \right\}$$

$$= a^2 + 2 \times 2 \cos 60° + 2 \times 2 \cos 120° \qquad \left\{ \begin{array}{l} \underline{a} . 2\underline{b} = 2\underline{a}.\underline{b} \\ = 4 \end{array} \right\}$$

$$= 4 + 2 - 2$$

$$= \underline{\underline{4}}$$

$\left\{ \text{N. B. The angle between } \underline{a} \text{ and } \underline{c} = 120° \right.$

4

Q10

$$\text{Let } f(x) = \sin 2x + \frac{2}{\sqrt{x}} = \sin 2x + 2x^{-\frac{1}{2}}$$

$$\Rightarrow f'(x) = 2\cos 2x - \frac{1}{2} \cdot 2 x^{-\frac{3}{2}}$$

$$= 2\cos 2x - \frac{1}{x\sqrt{x}} \quad \text{or} \quad 2\cos 2x - x^{-\frac{3}{2}}$$

Q11

Let $A\hat{O}x = \alpha^{\circ}$ and $B\hat{O}x = \beta^{\circ}$, then $A\hat{O}B = (\beta - \alpha)^{\circ}$

Then $\sin A\hat{O}B = \sin(\beta - \alpha)^{\circ}$

$$= \sin\beta\cos\alpha - \cos\beta\sin\alpha$$

$$= \frac{a}{\sqrt{(a^2+b^2)}} \cdot \frac{a}{\sqrt{(a^2+b^2)}} - \frac{b}{\sqrt{(a^2+b^2)}} \cdot \frac{b}{\sqrt{(a^2+b^2)}}$$

$$= \frac{a^2 - b^2}{a^2 + b^2}$$

$\left\{ \text{By Pythagoras; } OA = OB = \sqrt{(a^2+b^2)} \right\}$

Q12

$$y = x^2 - x$$

$$\frac{dy}{dx} = 2x - 1$$

$$1 + \frac{2y}{x} = 1 + \frac{2(x^2-x)}{x}$$

$$= 1 + 2x - 2$$

$$= 2x - 1$$

Hence $\dfrac{dy}{dx} = 1 + \dfrac{2y}{x}$

Q13

Let the required angle be θ°, $\Rightarrow \tan\theta^{\circ} = \dfrac{dy}{dx}$

$$y = x^3 - 4x - 5$$

$$\frac{dy}{dx} = 3x^2 - 4 \quad \Rightarrow \text{At } x = 2, \quad \frac{dy}{dx} = 3(2)^2 - 4 = 8$$

Hence $\tan\theta^{\circ} = 8$

$$\theta = 82.9^{\circ}$$

$$\doteqdot 83^{\circ}$$

Q14

(a) $f'(b) = 0$; $f'(d) = 0$ {gradient $= f'(x) = 0$}

$f'(0) = 1$ {gradient $= \tan^{-1}(45°)$}

(b) Since $f(x)$ is cubic,

Then $f'(x)$ is quadratic

i.e a parabola

with roots at $x = b$ and $x = d$

Q15

The maximum value of $4\cos(2\theta - \pi/4)$ is 4

When $4\cos(2\theta - \frac{\pi}{4}) = 4$

$\Rightarrow \cos(2\theta - \pi/4) = 1$

$2\theta - \pi/4 = 0$, 2π

$2\theta = \pi/4$, $9\frac{\pi}{4}$

$\theta = \frac{\pi}{8}$, $9\pi/8$

Q16

$\displaystyle\int_{1}^{2} \frac{u^2 + 2}{2u^2}\, du = \frac{1}{2}\int_{1}^{2}(1 + 2u^{-2})\, du$

$= \frac{1}{2}\left[u - 2u^{-1}\right]_{1}^{2}$

$= \frac{1}{2}\left((2-1) - (1-2)\right)$

$= \frac{1}{2}\cdot(2)$

$= 1$

{ N.B. It is usually easier to tackle problems like
this in the order A.B.C.; Algebra Before Calculus }

17

$$\left\{ \log_2 2x = \log_2 2 + \log_2 x = 1 + \log_2 x \right\}$$

The graph shows points $(1, 1)$, $(2, 2)$, $(4, 3)$, $(8, 4)$ on the curve $\log_2 2x = 1 + \log_2 x$, and the curve $\log_2 x$.

18

$$x - y = k \implies y = x - k \quad \text{and} \quad y^2 = x^2 - 2xk + k^2$$

$$x^2 + y^2 = 18 \implies x^2 + x^2 - 2xk + k^2 = 18 \quad \{\text{Substitution}\}$$

$$2x^2 - 2xk + k^2 - 18 = 0$$

This is a quadratic equation in x, where, $a = 2$; $b = -2k$; $c = k^2 - 18$

For Tangents $b^2 - 4ac = 0$ i.e. equal roots

$$\implies (-2k)^2 - 4(2)(k^2 - 18) = 0$$

$$4k^2 - 8k^2 + 144 = 0$$

$$4k^2 = 144$$

$$k^2 = 36$$

$$\underline{\underline{k = \pm 6}}$$

19

$$H(x) = g(f(x)) = g(2x + 3)$$

$$= \frac{(2x+3)^2 + 25}{(2x+3)^2 - 25}$$

$H(x)$ is undefined if $(2x+3)^2 - 25 = 0$ $\{ 2x^2 + 3 = 25 \}$

$$2x + 3 = \pm 5$$

$$2x = -8 \text{ or } 2$$

$$\underline{\underline{x = -4 \text{ or } 1}}$$

Q20

$$N(t) = 40\, e^{1.5t}$$

(a) At $t = 0$; $N(0) = 40\, e^0 = 40$

(b) At $N = 80$; $N(t) = 40\, e^{1.5t} = 80$

$$e^{1.5t} = 2$$

$$1.5t \log_e e = \log_e 2$$

$$1.5t = \log_e 2$$

$$t = \frac{\log_e 2}{1.5}$$

$$t = 0.462 \text{ h}$$

$$t \doteq 27.7 \text{ minutes}$$

Bacteria will take about <u>28 minutes</u> to double in number

---

Q21

Let $P_1 = 30$ and $P_2 =$ required sound intensity

$\{ P_2 \Rightarrow$ fire alarm$\}$

$$n = 10 \log_{10} \frac{P_2}{P_1}$$

$$\Rightarrow 6.5 = 10 \log_{10} \left(\frac{P_2}{30} \right)$$

$$\log_{10} \left(\frac{P_2}{30} \right) = 0.65$$

$\{$Take anti logs of both sides$\}$

$$\frac{P_2}{30} = 4.467$$

$$\underline{P_2 = 134.0 \text{ phons}}$$

8

Q1
(a)

At the y axis, $x = 0$; $f(0) = 0$

At the x axis, $y = 0$; $4x^2(x-3) = 0$

$$\Rightarrow x = 0 \text{ (twice)} \text{ or } x = 3$$

Hence the required points are $\underline{\underline{(0,0) \text{ and } (3,0)}}$

(b)

$$f(x) = 4x^2(x-3)$$
$$= 4x^3 - 12x^2$$

$$\left\{ \begin{array}{l} \text{For S.V.s} \\ \text{Put } f'(x) = 0 \end{array} \right\}$$

$$\Rightarrow f'(x) = 12x^2 - 24x = 0 \text{ at S.V.}$$

$$12x(x-2) = 0$$

$$x = 0 \text{ or } x = 2$$

where $y = 0$ or $y = -16$

Table of Values

x	$\rightarrow$	0	$\rightarrow$	$\rightarrow$	2	$\rightarrow$
$f'(x)$	+	0	−	−	0	+
shape	↗	→	↘	↘	→	↗

Max T.P. $\underline{\underline{(0,0)}}$ Min T.P. $\underline{\underline{(2,-16)}}$

(c)

$y = 4x^2(x-3)$

-16

$(2, -16)$

(d)

$$\text{Area} = -\int_0^3 (4x^2(x-3))\,dx = -\int_0^3 (4x^3 - 12x^2)\,dx$$

$$= -\left[x^4 - 4x^3 \right]_0^3$$

$$= \underline{\underline{27 \text{ units}^2}}$$

Q2

(a)
$$\underline{m} = \tfrac{1}{2}(\underline{a} + \underline{b}) = \tfrac{1}{2}\begin{pmatrix} 12 \\ 2 \\ 2 \end{pmatrix} = \begin{pmatrix} 6 \\ 1 \\ 1 \end{pmatrix}$$

$\Rightarrow$ M is the point $(6,1,1)$

{ Draw a diagram }

(b)
$$\underline{t} = \overrightarrow{OT}$$
$$= \overrightarrow{OC} + \overrightarrow{CT}$$
$$= \overrightarrow{OC} + \tfrac{2}{3}\overrightarrow{CM}$$
$$= \underline{c} + \tfrac{2}{3}(\underline{m} - \underline{c})$$
$$= \begin{pmatrix} 0 \\ 4 \\ 4 \end{pmatrix} + \tfrac{2}{3}\begin{pmatrix} 6 \\ -3 \\ -3 \end{pmatrix}$$
$$= \begin{pmatrix} 4 \\ 2 \\ 2 \end{pmatrix} \quad \Rightarrow \quad \text{T is the point } (4,2,2)$$

$\bullet\, O$

(c)
$$\overrightarrow{BT} = \underline{t} - \underline{b} = \begin{pmatrix} -4 \\ -1 \\ 3 \end{pmatrix} \qquad \overrightarrow{TD} = \underline{d} - \underline{t} = \begin{pmatrix} -8 \\ -2 \\ 6 \end{pmatrix}$$

since $\overrightarrow{BT} = \tfrac{1}{2}\,\overrightarrow{TD}$

Then B, T and D are collinear

And T divides BD in the ratio $1:2$

$\left\{ \begin{array}{l} BT \parallel TD \\ \text{and share the point T} \end{array} \right\}$

Q3

(a)
(i)
(ii)

(b) There are **3** roots to the equation $x^3 = 6x + 1$

(c) Estimate from the graph $x \doteq 2.5$; Let $f(x) = x^3 - (6x+1)$

$f(2.5) < 0 \quad f(2.6) > 0 \quad \Rightarrow \quad 2.5 < x < 2.6$

$f(2.525) < 0 \quad f(2.535) > 0 \Rightarrow 2.525 < x < 2.535 \Rightarrow \underline{x \doteq 2.53}$

Q4

(a)

(b) $3 - f(x) \geqslant 0$ for $0 \leqslant x \leqslant 2$ {From the graph}

(c) $g(x)$ has roots at $x = 0$ and $x = 2$
and a turning point at $(1, 2)$

$\Rightarrow \quad g(x) = a\,x\,(x-2)$ and $2 = a(1)(1-2)$

$\Rightarrow \quad a = -2$

Hence $\underline{g(x) = -2x\,(x-2)}$ {at $(1,2)$}

Q5

Total Length = 2 Circumferences + 2 Tangents

Eqn circle$_1$ is $x^2 + y^2 + 3y = 0$, $\Rightarrow$ centre $(0, -\tfrac{3}{2})$; radius $\tfrac{3}{2}$

Hence $C_1 = 2\pi \tfrac{3}{2} = \underline{\underline{3\pi}}$

For circle$_2$ the diameter = 4 $\Rightarrow$ radius = 2   {centre $(0, -2)$}

Hence $C_2 = 2\pi 2 = \underline{\underline{4\pi}}$

By Pythagoras

Each tangent is $\sqrt{12}$ units

$= 2\sqrt{3}$

2 tangents $= \underline{\underline{4\sqrt{3}}}$

Total Length $= \underline{\underline{7\pi + 4\sqrt{3} \text{ units}}}$

Q6

(a)

Let the level after n weeks $= U_n$ mg/ℓ

$U_0 = 20$ If 55% is removed, then 45% remains

$\Rightarrow U_1 = 0.45 U_0 + 26$ $= 35$

$U_2 = 0.45 U_1 + 26$ $= 41.75$

$U_3 = 0.45 U_2 + 26$ $= 44.7875$

$U_4 = 0.45 U_3 + 26$ $= 46.1544$

$U_5 = 0.45 U_4 + 26$ $= 46.7695$

$U_6 = 0.45 U_5 + 26$ $= 47.0463$

U_n appears to be approaching a fixed value $\doteq 47$

Let this "fixed" value $= \mu$

$$\Rightarrow \mu = 0.45\mu + 26$$

$$0.55\mu = 26$$

$$\mu = 47.273$$

i.e. In the long term the nitrate level will be $\doteq 47.3$ mg/ℓ

(b)   The <u>advice is acceptable</u> since $\mu < 50$, the recommended upper limit.

Q7

(a)

Area $=$ base $\times$ height   m^2 $\left\{ \begin{array}{l} B \text{ is the point} \\ (x, 9 - \frac{1}{4}x^2) \end{array} \right\}$

$= 2x \times \left(9 - \frac{x^2}{4} \right)$

$= \underline{18x - \frac{x^3}{2}}$ m^2

(b)   Let the Volume $= V(x) = $ length $\times$ area   m^3

$= 60 \left(18x - \frac{x^3}{2} \right)$

$$V(x) = 1080x - 30x^3$$

$$\Rightarrow V'(x) = 1080 - 90x^2 = 0 \quad \text{at S.V.}$$

$$90x^2 = 1080$$

$$x^2 = 12$$

$$x = \sqrt{12} \qquad \{\sqrt{12} = 2\sqrt{3} \div 3.46\}$$

$$V(\sqrt{12}) = 1080\sqrt{12} - 30(\sqrt{12})^3$$

$$= 1080\sqrt{12} - 360\sqrt{12}$$

$$= 720\sqrt{12}$$

$$= 1440\sqrt{3} \text{ m}^3 \quad \{\div 2494 \text{ m}^3\}$$

Table of Values

x	$\rightarrow$	$\sqrt{12}$	$\rightarrow$
$V'(x)$	+	0	−
shape	↗	→	↘

Max T.P.
at $x = \sqrt{12}$

Maximum Volume $= 1440\sqrt{3}$ m^3

Q8
(a)

$g(x) = \cos x$ is **EVEN** since $\cos(-x) = \cos x$

$h(x) = \sin x$ is <u>ODD</u> since $\sin 2(-x) = -\sin 2x$

(b)

$$\int_{-\frac{\pi}{2}}^{\frac{\pi}{2}} \cos x \, dx = \left[\sin x \right]_{-\frac{\pi}{2}}^{\frac{\pi}{2}} = \left((1) - (-1) \right) = \underline{\underline{2}}$$

$$\int_{-\frac{\pi}{2}}^{\frac{\pi}{2}} \sin 2x \, dx = \left[-\frac{\cos 2x}{2} \right]_{-\frac{\pi}{2}}^{\frac{\pi}{2}} = \left((\tfrac{1}{2}) - (\tfrac{1}{2}) \right) = \underline{\underline{0}}$$

(C)

(d)

$V(x) = x \cos x$

$V(-x) = -x\cos(-x) = -x\cos x = -V(x) \Rightarrow V(x)$ is <u>ODD</u>

Suggests that $\int_{-\frac{\pi}{2}}^{\frac{\pi}{2}} x \cos x \, dx = 0$ {½ turn symmetry}

13

Q9
(a)

Let $f(t) = \cos 30t° + \sqrt{3} \sin 30t° = k \cos(30t - \alpha)°$

$$= k \cos 30t° \cos\alpha° + k \sin 30t° \sin\alpha°$$

Hence $k \sin\alpha° = \sqrt{3} \implies k^2 \sin^2\alpha = 3$

$k \cos\alpha° = 1 \implies k^2 \cos^2\alpha = 1$

$$k^2 \sin^2\alpha + k^2 \cos^2\alpha = 3 + 1$$

$$k^2(\sin^2\alpha + \cos^2\alpha) = 4$$

$$k^2(1) = 4$$

$$\underline{\underline{k = 2}}$$

Also $\dfrac{k \sin\alpha°}{k \cos\alpha°} = \tan\alpha° = \sqrt{3}$

$$\underline{\underline{\alpha = 60}}$$

$\left\{ \begin{array}{l} \text{Reject } 240° \text{ as} \\ \sin\alpha° > 0 \text{ AND } \cos\alpha° > 0 \end{array} \right\}$

Hence $\underline{\underline{f(t) = 2\cos(30t - 60)°}}$

(b)
(i)

$f(t) = 2\cos(30t - 60)°$

(ii)

$d = 200 + 80(\cos 30t° + \sqrt{3} \sin 30t°)$

$d = 200 + 160 \cos(30t - 60)°$

14

(c)   "Low water" time is 0800 hr $\{at\ t=8\}$

(d)   From the graph $d \geqslant 150$ for $5.5 < t < 10.5$ approx.

Let $d = 200 + 160 \cos (30t - 60)° = 150$

$$160 \cos (30t - 60)° = -50$$
$$\cos (30t - 60)° = -0.3125$$
$$30t° - 60° = 108.2°, \ 251.8°$$
$$30t° = 168.2°, \ 311.8°$$
$$t = 5.6, \ 10.4$$
$$\text{Time} = 05.36 \quad \text{or} \quad 10.24$$

$\Rightarrow$ Fleet must avoid entering the harbour between

05.36 hr and 10.24 hr

•10
(a)

$$m_{PQ} = \tan 135° = -1$$

$$y = \frac{4}{x^2} = 4x^{-2}$$

$\left\{ \begin{array}{l} m = \tan \theta° \\[2mm] m = \dfrac{dy}{dx} \end{array} \right.$

$$\Rightarrow \frac{dy}{dx} = -8x^{-3} = -1 \quad \text{at the Pt of contact}$$

$$\frac{8}{x^3} = 1$$
$$x^3 = 8$$
$$x = 2$$
$$y = \frac{4}{2^2} = 1 \quad \Rightarrow \text{Pt of contact } (2,1)$$

(b)

Eqn $_{PQ}$ is $y - 1 = -1(x - 2)$

$$y = -x + 3$$
$$\underline{x + y = 3} \qquad \Rightarrow P \text{ is the point } (0,3)$$
$$Q \text{ is the point } (3,0)$$

At A ; $y = 3$ At B ; $x = 3$

$\Rightarrow \dfrac{4}{x^2} = 3$ $\Rightarrow y = \dfrac{4}{3^2} = \dfrac{4}{9}$

$x^2 = \dfrac{4}{3}$ $\Rightarrow \underline{B\left(3, \dfrac{4}{9}\right)}$

$x = \dfrac{2}{\sqrt{3}} \Rightarrow \underline{A\left(\dfrac{2}{\sqrt{3}}, 3\right)}$

The region OPABQ can be divided into 2 parts by the line $x = \dfrac{2}{\sqrt{3}}$ as shown:-

Area OPABQ $=$ Area of Rectangle $+$ Area under the curve

$$= \quad 3 \times \frac{2}{\sqrt{3}} \quad + \quad \int_{2/3}^{3} \frac{4}{x^2}\, dx$$

$$= \quad 2\sqrt{3} \quad + \quad \left[\frac{-4}{x} \right]_{\frac{2}{\sqrt{3}}}^{3}$$

$$= \quad 2\sqrt{3} \quad + \quad \left(\left(-\frac{4}{3} \right) - \left(-2\sqrt{3} \right) \right)$$

$$= \quad 4\sqrt{3} - \frac{4}{3} \quad \text{units}^2 \qquad \{5.59\text{u}^2\}$$

Shaded Area Required $= \quad 16\sqrt{3} - \dfrac{16}{3} \quad \text{units}^2 \qquad \{22.4\text{u}^2\}$

$$\{4 \times \text{Area OPABQ}\}$$

1 If $(x+3)$ is a factor of $f(x) = x^3 - x^2 + px + 15$

Then $f(-3) = 0$

$\left\{ \begin{array}{l} \text{Synthetic division takes} \\ \text{more work in this case} \end{array} \right\}$

$\Rightarrow (-3)^3 - (-3)^2 + p(-3) + 15 = 0$

$-27 - 9 - 3p + 15 = 0$

$$-3 \begin{array}{|cccc} 1 & -1 & p & 15 \end{array}$$

$-3p = 21$

$\underline{\underline{p = -7}}$

---

2 Let $f(x) = y = 4x^3 - 2$; $f(-1) = -6$

$\Rightarrow f'(x) = 12x^2$ Point of contact is $(-1, -6)$

$f'(-1) = 12 =$ gradient of tangent at $(-1, -6)$

Eqn tangent is $y + 6 = 12(x+1)$ $\{$ use $y - b = m(x-a)\}$

$$\underline{\underline{y = 12x + 6}}$$

Q3 Let M be the mid-point of AB $\Rightarrow$ M is the point $(1, 1)$

gradient $= \dfrac{3 - (-1)}{-2 - 4} = \dfrac{-2}{3}$ $\Rightarrow$ gradient $= \dfrac{3}{2}$
AB   diameter

Eqn. is $y - 1 = \dfrac{3}{2}(x-1)$ $\{$ use $y - b = m(x-a)\}$
diameter

$2y - 2 = 3x - 3$

$\underline{\underline{2y = 3x - 1}}$

Q4 $\overrightarrow{PQ} = \underline{q} - \underline{p} = \begin{pmatrix} 4 \\ 4 \\ 1 \end{pmatrix} - \begin{pmatrix} 2 \\ 2 \\ 3 \end{pmatrix} = \begin{pmatrix} 2 \\ 2 \\ -2 \end{pmatrix}$

$\overrightarrow{QR} = \underline{r} - \underline{q} = \begin{pmatrix} 5 \\ 5 \\ 0 \end{pmatrix} - \begin{pmatrix} 4 \\ 4 \\ 1 \end{pmatrix} = \begin{pmatrix} 1 \\ 1 \\ -1 \end{pmatrix}$

Since $\overrightarrow{PQ} = 2\overrightarrow{QR}$ then P, Q and R are collinear

And Q divides PR in the ratio $\underline{\underline{2:1}}$

Q5
(a)

$$\vec{BC} = \begin{pmatrix} 4 \\ 2 \\ -3 \end{pmatrix}$$

(b)

$$|\vec{BC}| = \sqrt{(4^2 + 2^2 + (-3)^2)}$$

$$= \sqrt{29} \doteq 5.4$$

Q6

$$\int_{1}^{2} (3x^2 + 4)\, dx = \left[x^3 + 4x \right]_{1}^{2}$$

$$= ((8+8) - (1+4))$$

$$= 11 \text{ units}^2$$

$y = 3x^2 + 4$

Q7

Eqn is $x^2 + y^2 - 10x - 12y + 45 = 0$
body

Centre $(5,6)$; radius $= \sqrt{(5^2 + 6^2 - 45)}$

$$= \sqrt{16}$$

$$= 4 \quad \Rightarrow \text{ diameter } = 8$$
body

diameter + diameter $= 14$
body   head

$\Rightarrow$ diameter $= 6 \quad \Rightarrow$ radius $= 3$
head   head

Let Centre head $= (a, b) \Rightarrow a = 5$

$$\Rightarrow b = 6 + 4 + 3 = 13$$

Eqn. head is $(x - 5)^2 + (y - 13)^2 = 3^2$

$$x^2 - 10x + 25 + y^2 - 26y + 169 = 9$$

$$x^2 + y^2 - 10x - 26y + 185 = 0$$

Q8

$$f(x) = \int f'(x)\, dx = \int (1-2x)\, dx$$
$$= x - x^2 + c$$

At $(2, 1)$; $\quad 1 = 2 - (2)^2 + c$
$$1 = -2 + c$$
$$c = 3$$

Hence $f(x) = -x^2 + x + 3$

Q9

$\cos D = \dfrac{2}{\sqrt{5}}$

$\sin D = \sqrt{(1 - \cos^2 D)}$

$\quad = \sqrt{\left(1 - \dfrac{4}{5}\right)}$

$\quad = \dfrac{1}{\sqrt{5}}$

$\left\{ \begin{array}{l} \text{Draw a diagram} \\ \text{Use Pythagoras} \end{array} \right\}$

$\cos 2D = \cos^2 D - \sin^2 D$

$\quad = \dfrac{4}{5} - \dfrac{1}{5}$

$\quad = \dfrac{3}{5}$

$\left\{ \begin{array}{l} \text{OR} \\ \cos 2D = 2\cos^2 D - 1 \\ \quad = 1 - 2\sin^2 D \end{array} \right\}$

Q10
(a)

From the graph; the amplitude is 2
the period is $90° \Rightarrow$ the frequency is 4
the equation is $y = 2 \sin 4x°$

(b)

$2 \sin 4x° = -1.5$
$\sin 4x° = -0.75$
$4x° = 228.6, \quad 311.4$
$x = 57.1 \quad , \quad 77.9$

Hence A is the point $(57.1, -1.5)$; B is the point $(77.9, -1.5)$

Q11

Stationary points on $y = f(x)$

$\Rightarrow$ Roots of $y = f'(x)$

$f(x)$ increasing; $0 < x < 2$

$\Rightarrow f'(x) > 0$; $0 < x < 2$

Q12

$$\begin{pmatrix} a \\ b \\ 1 \end{pmatrix} \cdot \begin{pmatrix} 1 \\ -1 \\ 1 \end{pmatrix} = 0 \qquad\qquad \begin{pmatrix} a \\ b \\ 1 \end{pmatrix} \cdot \begin{pmatrix} -2 \\ 1 \\ 1 \end{pmatrix} = 0 \qquad \{\text{scalar product}\}$$

$\Rightarrow \underline{a - b + 1 = 0} \quad ①$ $\qquad\qquad \Rightarrow \underline{-2a + b + 1 = 0} \quad ②$

Adding $① + ②$ $\qquad -a + 2 = 0$

$\qquad\qquad\qquad\qquad \underline{a = 2}$

$\qquad\qquad\qquad\qquad \Rightarrow \underline{\underline{b = 3}}$ $\qquad \{\text{By substitution}\}$

Q13
(a)

They meet where :-

$y = 4 - 2x^2 = 2x^2$

$4x^2 = 4$

$x = \pm 1$

$y = 2$

$\Rightarrow$ Meeting points are $\underline{(-1, 2) \text{ and } (1, 2)}$ $\qquad \{\text{Draw a diagram}\}$

(b)

$$\text{Area} = \int_{-1}^{1} \left((4 - 2x^2) - (2x^2) \right) dx$$

$$= 2 \int_{0}^{1} (4 - 4x^2) \, dx \qquad \{\text{By symmetry}\}$$

$$= 2 \left[4x - 4\frac{x^3}{3} \right]_{0}^{1}$$

$$= 2 \left(\frac{8}{3} \right)$$

$\Rightarrow \text{Area} = \underline{\underline{\frac{16}{3}}} \text{ units}^2$ $\qquad\qquad (\doteq 5.33 \text{ units}^2)$

Q14

"Straight line" $\Rightarrow$ $\log_{10} y = m \log_{10} x + c$

"gradient of 2" $\Rightarrow$ $m = 2$

• passes through $(0,1) \Rightarrow c = 1$

let $c = \log_{10} A = 1$

$\qquad \Rightarrow A = 10$

Hence

$\log_{10} y = 2 \log_{10} x + 1$

$\log_{10} y = 2 \log_{10} x + \log_{10} 10 \qquad \{n \log x = \log x^n\}$

$\log_{10} y = \log_{10} x^2 + \log_{10} 10$

$\log_{10} y = \log_{10} (10 x^2)$

$\underline{\underline{y = 10 x^2}} \qquad \{\log a + \log b = \log ab\}$

Q15

$2 \cos^2 x = \frac{1}{2}$

$\cos^2 x = \frac{1}{4}$

$\cos x = \pm \frac{1}{2}$

$\underline{\underline{x = \frac{\pi}{3}, \frac{2\pi}{3}}}$

Q16

$f(x) = \frac{1}{3} x^3 - 2x^2 - 5x - 4$

$f'(x) = x^2 - 4x - 5 \qquad > 0$ for $f(x)$ increasing

$(x+1)(x-5) > 0 \qquad \{\text{Draw a diagram}\}$

$\underline{\underline{x < -1 \ \text{or} \ x > 5}}$

21

Q17

{Move 2 units to the right}

$y = \log_{10}(x-2)$

(10, 1)
(12, 1)

Q18

Here $a = (k-2)$; $b = -(3k-2)$; $c = 2k$

{Examine $b^2 - 4ac$}

$b^2 - 4ac = (-(3k-2))^2 - 4(k-2)(2k)$

$= 9k^2 - 12k + 4 - 8k^2 + 16k$

$= k^2 + 4k + 4$

$= (k+2)^2 \geqslant 0$ for all k {perfect square $\geqslant 0$}

Hence roots are real since $b^2 - 4ac \geqslant 0$

Q19

$f(x) = \cos^2 x - \dfrac{2}{3x^2} = (\cos x)^2 - \dfrac{2}{3}x^{-2}$

{$\sin 2x = 2\sin x \cos x$}

$\Rightarrow f'(x) = 2\cos x(-\sin x) - (-2)\dfrac{2}{3}x^{-3}$

$= -\sin 2x + \dfrac{4}{3x^3}$

Q20

Gradient $= \tan A\hat{O}R$

In $\triangle AOB$; $\tan A\hat{O}B = \dfrac{3}{4}$

$\Rightarrow A\hat{O}B = 36.9°$

In $\triangle BOR$, $R\hat{B}O = 90°$ (OC is a diameter)

$\Rightarrow \cos B\hat{O}R = \dfrac{5}{13}$

$\Rightarrow B\hat{O}R = 67.4°$

Hence $A\hat{O}R = A\hat{O}B + B\hat{O}R = 104.3°$

$\Rightarrow$ gradient $= -3.9$ ($\doteqdot -4$)

{Alternative method
Knowing

$\tan A\hat{O}R = \dfrac{\tan A\hat{O}B + \tan B\hat{O}R}{1 - \tan A\hat{O}B \tan B\hat{O}R}$

$= \dfrac{\frac{3}{4} + \frac{12}{5}}{1 - \frac{3}{4} \cdot \frac{12}{5}}$

$= -3\frac{15}{16}$

$\doteqdot -4$ }

Q1
(a)

$$f(x) = (x-1)^2(x+2)$$

$f(0) = 2 \implies$ crosses the y axis at $\underline{(0,2)}$

$f(x) = 0 \implies (x-1)^2(x+2) = 0$

$\implies x = 1$ (twice), $x = -2$

$\implies$ crosses the x axis at $\underline{(-2,0)}$

touches the x axis at $\underline{(1,0)}$

(b)

$$f(x) = (x-1)^2(x+2) = (x^2 - 2x + 1)(x+2)$$

$$= x^3 - 3x + 2$$

$\implies f'(x) = 3x^2 - 3 = 0$ at S.V.

$$3(x^2-1) = 0 \qquad \{x = \pm 1\}$$
$$x^2 = 1$$

$$x = -1 ; \quad x = 1$$

$\implies y = 4 \qquad y = 0 \qquad$ Table of Values

x	$\rightarrow$	-1	$\rightarrow$	$\rightarrow$	1	$\rightarrow$
$f'(x)$	$+$	0	$-$	$-$	0	$+$
shape	↗	→	↘	↘	→	↗

Max T.P. $\qquad$ Min T.P.
$\underline{(-1,4)} \qquad\qquad \underline{(1,0)}$

(c)

$$y = (x-1)^2(x+2)$$

(−1, 4)

4

2

−2 −1 O (1, 0) x

y

x

Q2

(a) $\text{gradient}_{PR} = \dfrac{14-(-2)}{9-1} = 2 \quad \Rightarrow \quad m_{QS} = -\dfrac{1}{2} \qquad \{m_{PR} \times m_{QS} = -1\}$

$\{\text{Draw a diagram}\}$

Eqn_{PR} is; $y - (-2) = 2(x-1)$

$$\underline{y = 2x - 4} \quad \text{①}$$

Eqn_{QS} is; $y - 3 = -\dfrac{1}{2}(x-6)$

$$2y - 6 = -x + 6$$

$$\underline{x + 2y = 12} \quad \text{②}$$

Eqn ① × 2 can be written $2y = 4x - 8$

Eqn ② can be written $2y = -x + 12$

$$\overline{0 = 5x - 20}$$

$$\Rightarrow x = 4$$
$$y = 4$$

Hence diagonals meet at $\underline{\underline{(4,4)}}$

(b) Let M be the point $(4,4)$ $\qquad \{\text{mid point of PR is } (5,6)\}$

This is NOT the mid point of PR $\Rightarrow$ M is the mid point of QS

Then $\vec{QM} = \vec{MS} = \vec{QM}$

$$\underline{s} - \underline{m} = \underline{m} - \underline{q}$$

$$\underline{s} = 2\underline{m} - \underline{q}$$

$$\underline{s} = 2\binom{4}{4} - \binom{6}{3}$$

$$\underline{s} = \binom{2}{5}$$

$$\Rightarrow \text{S is the point } \underline{\underline{(2,5)}}$$

Q3

(a)

Tuesday 20th to Sunday 25th = 5 days

Let T_n = Total n days from Tuesday 20th

$\Rightarrow T_1 = 1.08\,T_0$ $\qquad${ 108% of previous day's total}

$\qquad T_2 = 1.08\,T_1 = 1.08^2\,T_0$ $\qquad\qquad T_0 = 50$

$\qquad T_3 = 1.08\,T_2 = 1.08^3\,T_0$

$\Rightarrow T_n = 1.08^n\,T_0$

$\qquad T_5 = 1.08^5 \times 50 = 73.47$

$\qquad\qquad$ Hence about <u>73 people affected</u>

(b)

$T_7 = 1.08^7 \times 50 = 85.69$

Hence about 86 people affected BEFORE inoculations.

If Daily decrease is 21%, then 79% still affected

Let A_n = Total affected n days after inoculations

$\qquad\qquad\qquad$ i.e. n days after Tuesday 27th

$\qquad A_1 = 0.79\,A_0$

$\qquad A_2 = 0.79\,A_1 = 0.79^2\,A_0$

$\qquad A_3 = 0.79\,A_2 = 0.79^3\,A_0$

$\Rightarrow A_n = 0.79^n\,A_0$ $\qquad\qquad A_0 = 86$

As Tuesday 27th to Saturday 31st = 4 days

$\qquad A_4 = 0.79^4 \times 86 = 33.50$

$\qquad$ Hence about <u>33 people</u> still affected

25

Q4

(a)
$$\underline{g} = \overrightarrow{OG} = \overrightarrow{OB} + \overrightarrow{BG} = \overrightarrow{OB} + \frac{2}{3}\overrightarrow{BM}$$

{ M is $(6, 18, 12)$ }

ie $\left(\frac{9+3}{2}, \frac{9+27}{2}, \frac{24+0}{2}\right)$

$$= \underline{b} + \frac{2}{3}(\underline{m} - \underline{b})$$

$$= \frac{1}{3}\underline{b} + \frac{2}{3}\underline{m}$$

$$= \frac{1}{3}\begin{pmatrix} 27 \\ 3 \\ 0 \end{pmatrix} + \frac{2}{3}\begin{pmatrix} 6 \\ 18 \\ 12 \end{pmatrix}$$

$$= \begin{pmatrix} 9 \\ 1 \\ 0 \end{pmatrix} + \begin{pmatrix} 4 \\ 12 \\ 8 \end{pmatrix}$$

$$= \begin{pmatrix} 13 \\ 13 \\ 8 \end{pmatrix} \quad \Rightarrow \text{ G is the point } \underline{\underline{(13, 13, 8)}}$$

(b)
$$\cos A\hat{O}G = \frac{\overrightarrow{OA}.\overrightarrow{OG}}{|\overrightarrow{OA}||\overrightarrow{OG}|}$$

$9 \times 13 + 9 \times 13 + 24 \times 8 = 426$

$9^2 + 9^2 + 24^2 = 738$

$13^2 + 13^2 + 8^2 = 402$

$$= \frac{\begin{pmatrix} 9 \\ 9 \\ 24 \end{pmatrix} . \begin{pmatrix} 13 \\ 13 \\ 8 \end{pmatrix}}{\sqrt{738}\,\sqrt{402}}$$

$$= \frac{426}{544.7}$$

$$\doteqdot 0.782$$

$$A\hat{O}G \doteqdot 38.6°$$ { 38.5° if more figures kept }

Required angle about $39°$
$\underline{\underline{}}$

Q5

(a)
$$2\cos(x+30)° - \sin x° = 2\cos x°\cos 30° - 2\sin x° \sin 30° - \sin x°$$

$$= 2\cos x°.\frac{\sqrt{3}}{2} - 2\sin x°.\frac{1}{2} - \sin x$$

$$= \underline{\underline{\sqrt{3}\cos x° - 2\sin x°}}$$

(b) Let $\sqrt{3}\cos x° - 2\sin x° = k\cos(x+\alpha)°$

$$= k\cos x° \cos\alpha° - k\sin x° \sin\alpha°$$

Q5
(b)
CONT.

$k\cos d = \sqrt{3}$; $-k\sin d = -2$

$k^2\cos^2 d = 3$ $\qquad k^2\sin^2 d = 4$ $\qquad \Rightarrow k^2 = 3+4$

$$\underline{k = \sqrt{7}} \quad \{\doteq 2.65\}$$

$\tan d^\circ = \dfrac{k\sin d^\circ}{k\cos d^\circ} = \dfrac{2}{\sqrt{3}} \quad \Rightarrow \quad \underline{d = 49.1}$

$$\underline{\sqrt{3}\cos x - 2\sin x^\circ = \sqrt{7}\cos(x+49.1)^\circ}$$

(c)

$2\cos(x+30)^\circ = \sin x^\circ + 1$

$\Rightarrow 2\cos(x+30)^\circ - \sin x^\circ = 1$ $\qquad$ from part (a)

$\Rightarrow \sqrt{7}\cos(x+49.1)^\circ = 1$ $\qquad$ from part (b)

$\cos(x+49.1)^\circ = \dfrac{1}{\sqrt{7}}$ $\qquad \{\doteq 0.378\}$

$x^\circ + 49.1^\circ = 67.8^\circ, 292.2^\circ$

$\underline{x = 18.7, 243.1}$

Q6
(a)

$f(x) = x^3 - 2x^2 - 5x + 6$; $g(x) = x-1 \Rightarrow f(g(x)) = f(x-1)$

$f(x-1) = (x-1)^3 - 2(x-1)^2 - 5(x-1) + 6$

$= x^3 - 3x^2 + 3x - 1 - 2x^2 + 4x - 2 - 5x + 5 + 6$

$= \underline{x^3 - 5x^2 + 2x + 8}$

(b)

By synthetic division:

$$
\begin{array}{r|rrrr}
2 & 1 & -5 & 2 & 8 \\
  &   & 2 & -6 & -8 \\
4 & 1 & -3 & -4 & \underline{0} \quad \Rightarrow (x-2)\text{ is a factor} \\
  &   & 4 & 4 & \\
  & 1 & 1 & \underline{0} & \Rightarrow (x-4) \text{ is a factor}
\end{array}
$$

$(x+1)$ is a factor

Hence $f(g(x)) = \underline{(x+1)(x-2)(x-4)}$

(c) $k(x) = \dfrac{1}{f(g(x))} = \dfrac{1}{(x+1)(x-2)(x-4)}$ $\qquad x \neq -1, 2, 4$

Not defined for $\underline{x = -1, 2 \text{ or } 4}$ $\qquad \{\text{If } x = -1, 2 \text{ or } 4 \text{ then } f(g(x)) = 0\}$

Q7
(a)

$$y^2 = x$$

$$\Rightarrow y = \sqrt{x} \quad \text{meets} \quad y = x^2 \quad \text{where} \quad \sqrt{x} = x^2$$

$$\Rightarrow x = 0 \; ; \; x = 1$$

Area between the curves
can be represented by

(i) $\displaystyle\int_0^k (\sqrt{x} - x^2)\,dx$

(ii) $\displaystyle\int_k^1 (\sqrt{x} - x^2)\,dx$

(b)

$$\int_0^k (\sqrt{x} - x^2)\,dx = \int_k^1 (\sqrt{x} - x^2)\,dx$$

$$\left[\frac{2x^{3/2}}{3} - \frac{x^3}{3}\right]_0^k = \left[\frac{2x^{3/2}}{3} - \frac{x^3}{3}\right]_k^1$$

$$\frac{2}{3}k^{3/2} - \frac{k^3}{3} = \left(\frac{2}{3} - \frac{1}{3}\right) - \left(\frac{2}{3}k^{3/2} - \frac{k^3}{3}\right)$$

$$\frac{4}{3}k^{3/2} - \frac{2}{3}k^3 - \frac{1}{3} = 0$$

$$\underline{2k^3 - 4k^{3/2} + 1 = 0}$$

(c)

Let $p^2 = k^3 \qquad$ Eqn is $2p^2 - 4p + 1 = 0$

$$\Rightarrow p = k^{3/2}$$

$$p = \frac{4 \pm \sqrt{(16-8)}}{4}$$

$$p \doteqdot 0.293$$

If $k^3 = p^2 \qquad\qquad\qquad$ {ignore 1·707}

Then $k = p^{2/3} \quad \Rightarrow \quad \underline{\underline{k \doteqdot 0.441}} \quad$ $\left\{\begin{array}{l}\text{ignore } 1\cdot42\\ \text{value} > 1\end{array}\right\}$

Q8
(a)

Eqn is $x^2 + y^2 - 8x + 2y - 19 = 0 \;\Rightarrow\; $ Centre $(4, -1)$
outer circle

$$\text{radius} = \sqrt{(4^2 + (-1)^2 + 19)}$$

Base line is a tangent

$$= 6$$

$$\Rightarrow \text{radius} \qquad = 5 \text{ units} \quad \{y = -6 \text{ is 5 units from centre}\}$$
inner circle

Eqn is. $(x-4)^2 + (y-(-1))^2 = 5^2 \;$ or $\; \underline{\underline{x^2 + y^2 - 8x + 2y - 8 = 0.}}$
inner circle

28

Q8
(b)

$$3x - 4y + 9 = 0$$

$$3x = 4y - 9$$

$$x = \frac{4y-9}{3} \qquad \Rightarrow x^2 = \frac{16y^2 - 72y + 81}{9}$$

By substitution

$$x^2 + y^2 - 8x + 2y - 8 = 0$$

$$\frac{16y^2 - 72y + 81}{9} + y^2 - 8\left(\frac{4y-9}{3}\right) + 2y - 8 = 0$$

$$16y^2 - 72y + 81 + 9y^2 - 96y + 216 + 18y - 72 = 0$$

$$25y^2 - 150y + 225 = 0$$

$$y^2 - 6y + 9 = 0$$

$$(y-3)^2 = 0$$

$$y = 3 \quad \text{(twice)} \quad \underline{\text{Equal Roots} \Rightarrow \text{tangent}}$$

By substitution $x = 1 \qquad \Rightarrow \underline{\text{Point of contact is } (1,3)}$

Q9
(a)

$$f(x) = x^3 - 2x^2 + 6x - 4$$

$$f(0) = -4 \quad \Rightarrow f(0) < 0$$

$$f(1) = 1 \quad \Rightarrow f(1) > 0$$

Hence $f(x)$ has a root
$\qquad\qquad \underline{\text{between 0 and 1}}$

(b)

$$q = p - \frac{f(p)}{f'(p)} \qquad\qquad f'(x) = 3x^2 - 4x + 6$$

choose $p = 0 \quad \Rightarrow f(p) = -4 \; ; \; f'(p) = 6$ and $q = \frac{2}{3}$

Table of values

Estimate	p	$f(p)$	$f'(p)$	$q = p - \frac{f(p)}{f'(p)}$
1	0	-4	6	0.6667
2	0.6667	-0.5924	3.7777	0.7937
3	0.7937	-0.0023	3.4552	0.7932
{ 4	0.7932	-0.0001	3.4564	0.7932 }

Estimates 2 and 3 agree to 1 dec. place $\Rightarrow$ Root is $\underline{x \doteq 0.8}$

$\{ x = 0.7932 \text{ to } 4\,\text{d.p.} \}$

Q10
(a)   Frequency $= \pi/6 \Rightarrow$ Period $= \frac{2\pi}{\pi/6} = 12$

(b)

(c)   We require $w(t) - 0.25 = 0$ for reservoir to run dry

$$1.1 - \sin \frac{\pi}{6} t - 0.25 = 0$$

$$\sin \frac{\pi}{6} t = 0.85$$

$$\frac{\pi}{6} t = 1.02, 2.13, 7.30, 8.41, 13.59, 14.69$$

$$t = 1.94, 4.06, 13.94, 16.06, 25.94, 28.06$$

Since 1st April 1990 $\Rightarrow t = 23$, Take the first $t > 23$

i.e. $t \doteq 25.94$

$t \doteq 25.94 \Rightarrow$ Required date is <u>28th June 1990</u>

30

Q1

$$3x + 2y - 5 = 0$$

$$\Rightarrow \quad y = -\frac{3}{2}x + \frac{5}{2} \quad \left\{\text{Put into the form } y = mx+c\right\}$$

$$\Rightarrow \quad \text{gradient} = -\frac{3}{2}$$

If lines are parallel then $m_1 = m_2$

Eqn$_{\text{line}}$ is $\quad y - (-5) = -\frac{3}{2}(x-3) \quad \left\{\text{use } y - b = m(x-a)\right\}$

$$2y + 10 = -3x + 9$$

$$\underline{3x + 2y + 1 = 0}$$

Q2

$$\text{Gradient}_{AB} = \frac{4b^2 - a^2}{2b - 9} = \frac{(2b+a)(2b-a)}{2b-a} \quad \left\{\text{Factorise}\right\}$$

$$\Rightarrow \underline{m_{AB} = 2b + a}$$

Q3

$$\underline{a} = \begin{pmatrix} 2 \\ 3 \\ -1 \end{pmatrix} \; ; \; \underline{b} = \begin{pmatrix} 3 \\ -1 \\ 3 \end{pmatrix} \qquad \left\{\text{Use the scalar product}\right\}$$

$$\underline{a} \cdot \underline{b} = 2 \times 3 + 3 \times (-1) + (-1) \times 3 = 0$$

$$\Rightarrow \underline{a \text{ and } b \text{ are perpendicular}}$$

Q4
(a)

$$y = k\, e^{0.5x}$$

$$\text{at } x = 0; \; y = k\, e^0 = 3 \qquad \left\{e^0 = 1\right\}$$

$$\underline{k = 3}$$

(b)

$$y = 3\, e^{0.5x}$$

$$\text{at } x = 1; \; y = 3\, e^{0.5}$$

$$= 3 \times 1.6487$$

$$\doteqdot \underline{4.95} \quad \Rightarrow \underline{P \text{ is the point } (1, 4.95)}$$

Q5

Let $y = f(x) = 3x^2 + 2$ then $f(1) = 5$

$\Rightarrow f'(x) = 6x \quad \Rightarrow \quad f'(1) = 6 \qquad \{m = f'(x)\}$

Eqn. is $\quad y - 5 = 6(x-1) \qquad \{\text{use } y - b = m(x-a)\}$
tangent

$\underline{y = 6x - 1}$

Q6

If remainder $= 114$ when $f(x)$ is divided by $(x-2)$

Then $f(2) = 114$

$$
\begin{array}{r|ccccc}
2 & 2 & -1 & P & q & 12 \\
  &   & 4 & 6 & 2(P+6) & 2q+4p+24 \\
\hline
  & 2 & 3 & p+6 & q+2p+12 & 2q+4p+36 = 114 \qquad \{2q+4p = 78\}
\end{array}
$$

$$\underline{q + 2p = 39} \tag{1}$$

If $(x+1)$ is a factor of $f(x)$, then $f(-1) = 0$

$$
\begin{array}{r|ccccc}
-1 & 2 & -1 & P & q & 12 \\
   &   & -2 & 3 & -P-3 & -q+p+3 \\
\hline
   & 2 & -3 & p+3 & qp-3 & -q+p+15 = 0
\end{array}
$$

$$\underline{-q + p = -15} \tag{2}$$

$\text{(1)} + \text{(2)} \Rightarrow 3p = 24$

$p = 8$

$\Rightarrow q = 23 \qquad \{\text{By substitution in (2)}\}$

$\underline{\underline{\text{Hence } p = 8 \text{ and } q = 23}}$

Q7
(a)

$\overrightarrow{LM} = \underline{m} - \underline{\ell} = \begin{pmatrix} 12 \\ -8 \\ 4 \end{pmatrix} \; ; \; \overrightarrow{MN} = \underline{n} - \underline{m} = \begin{pmatrix} 3 \\ -2 \\ 1 \end{pmatrix}$

Since $\overrightarrow{LM} = 4\overrightarrow{MN}$ then $\underline{L, M \text{ and } N \text{ are collinear}}$

(b)

Since $\overrightarrow{LM} = 4\overrightarrow{MN}$ then $\qquad \{\text{Parallel and share M}\}$

Thr.. $\underline{M \text{ divides } LN \text{ in the ratio } 4:1}$

Q8

$$x^2 + y^2 - 4x + 6y - 4 = 0 \quad \Rightarrow \quad \text{centre } (2, -3)$$

point of contact $(3, 1)$

$$\frac{\text{Gradient}}{\text{radius}} \quad = \quad \frac{1-(-3)}{3-2} = 4$$

$$\Rightarrow \quad \frac{\text{Gradient}}{\text{tangent}} \quad = \quad -\frac{1}{4} \qquad \{m_1 \times m_2 = -1\}$$

$$\frac{\text{Eqn}}{\text{tangent}} \quad \text{is} \quad y - 1 = -\frac{1}{4}(x-3) \qquad \{\text{use } y-b = m(x-a)\}$$

$$4y - 4 = -x + 3$$

$$\underline{x + 4y = 7}$$

Q9

(a)

$\{\text{Reflect in } x\text{-axis}\}$

$y = f(x)$

$y = -f(x)$

$\{\text{T.Ps on } f(x) \Rightarrow \text{roots of } f'(x)\}$

(b)

$y = f'(x)$

$y = f(x)$

Q10

$$f(x) = \int f'(x)\, dx$$

$$= \int (4x^3 - 1)\, dx = \underline{x^4 - x + C} \quad \{\text{General solution}\}$$

$$f(2) = -1 \Rightarrow \quad (2)^4 - (2) + C = -1$$

$$16 - 2 + C = -1$$

$$C = -15$$

Hence $\underline{f(x) = x^4 - x - 15}$ $\{\text{Particular solution}\}$

Q11

$18 - 13 = 5\text{ years.}$ $\qquad 9\% = 0.09$

Let $A_n = $ Amount of money n years after it is invested

$$A_1 = 1.09\, A_0$$

$$A_2 = 1.09\, A_1 = 1.09^2 A_0$$

$$A_3 = 1.09\, A_2 = 1.09^3 A_0$$

$$A_n = 1.09^n A_0 \Rightarrow A_5 = 1.09^5 A_0$$

$$= 1.539\, A_0$$

Hence increase on the investment $\doteqdot \underline{54\%}$

Q12

$$\sin 2A = 2 \sin A \cos A$$

$$= 2 \cdot \frac{3}{4} \cdot \frac{\sqrt{7}}{4}$$

$$= \underline{\underline{\frac{3\sqrt{7}}{8}}}$$

$\{\text{Draw a diagram}\}$
use Pythagoras

4   3

A

$\sqrt{7}$

(By Pythagoras)

Q13

$$f(x) = 5(7 - 2x)^3$$

$$f'(x) = 3 \times 5(7 - 2x)^2 \cdot (-2)$$

$$= -30(7 - 2x)^2$$

$$\Rightarrow f'(4) = -30(7 - 2(4))^2 = \underline{-30}$$

34

Q14
(a) Between B and E $\Rightarrow$ $-2 \leqslant x \leqslant 2$

(b) Between A and B $\Rightarrow$ $-4 < x < -2$

Q15
(a)
$$7 - 2x - x^2 = 7 + 1 - 1 - 2x - x^2$$
$$= 8 - (1 + 2x + x^2) \qquad \{\text{complete the square}\}$$
$$= 8 - (x+1)^2$$
$$\Rightarrow a = 8 \; ; \; b = 1$$

(b)
Maximum Value of $7 - 2x - x^2$ is $\underline{8}$ \qquad Max T.P at $(-1, 8)$

Since Maximum Value of $8 - (x+1)^2$ is 8 \quad at $x = -1$, $(x+1)^2 = 0$

$$\left\{ \begin{array}{l} \text{Using calculus } f(x) = 7 - 2x - x^2 \\ \qquad\qquad f'(x) = -2 - 2x = 0 \text{ at S.V.} \\ \qquad\qquad\qquad x = -1 \end{array} \right\}$$

Axis of symmetry of the parabola is $x = -1 \Rightarrow y = 8$

Q16
(a)
$$\int_1^2 (4 - x^2)\, dx = \left[4x - \frac{x^3}{3} \right]_1^2$$
$$= \left(8 - \frac{8}{3} \right) - \left(4 - \frac{1}{3} \right)$$
$$= \frac{5}{3} \qquad\qquad \{1 \cdot 67\}$$

(b)

Area $= \frac{5}{3}$ units^2

35

Q17

$$\underline{b} \cdot (\underline{a} + \underline{b} + \underline{c})$$

$$= \underline{b} \cdot \underline{a} + \underline{b} \cdot \underline{b} + \underline{b} \cdot \underline{c}$$

$$= 0 + |\underline{b}|^2 + |\underline{b}||\underline{c}| \cos 45°$$

$$= 2^2 + 2 \cdot 2\sqrt{2} \cdot \frac{1}{\sqrt{2}}$$

$$= 4 + 4$$

$$= \underline{8}$$

By Pythagoras

$$2 \quad 45° \quad 2\sqrt{2}$$
$$45°$$
$$2$$

$$\left\{ \begin{array}{l} \text{Alternatively since } \underline{a} + \underline{c} = \underline{b} \\ \text{We have } \underline{b} \cdot (2\underline{b}) = 2b = 8 \end{array} \right\}$$

Q18

In the equation $kx^2 + 3x + 3 = k$ let $a = k$

$$kx^2 + 3x + 3 - k = 0 \quad \text{let } b = 3$$
$$\text{let } c = 3 - k$$

$$b^2 - 4ac = 3^2 - 4(k)(3-k)$$

$$= 9 + 4k^2 - 12k$$

$$= (2k - 3)^2 \quad \text{a perfect square} \geqslant 0$$

Since $b^2 - 4ac \geqslant 0$, then the roots of the equation are REAL

Q19

(a)

$$f(x) = 2x + 5 \Rightarrow f(p) = 2p + 5 = 7 \; ; \quad g(x) = x^2 - 3$$

$$2p = 2 \qquad\qquad g(7) = 7^2 - 3$$
$$p = 1 \qquad\qquad\quad 7 = 46$$

(b)

$$h(x) = g(f(x))$$

$$= (2x^2 + 5)^2 - 3$$

$$= 4x^2 + 20x + 22 \qquad \left\{ \text{check } h(1) = 46 \right\}$$

Q20

A is the point where $\cos 2x° = 1 + \sin x°$

$$\cos 2x° - \sin x° - 1 = 0$$

$$1 - 2\sin^2 x° - \sin x° - 1 = 0$$

$$2 \sin^2 x° + \sin x° = 0$$

$$\sin x° (2\sin x° + 1) = 0$$

$$\sin x° = 0 \; ; \quad \sin x° = -\tfrac{1}{2} \quad \{\text{At } A, 180 < x < 270\}$$

$$x = 0, 180, 210, 330$$

$$\Rightarrow \underline{x = 210} \text{ at } A \qquad \left\{ \text{The point } A \, (210, \tfrac{1}{2}) \right\}$$

Q1 (a)

Let $y = f(x) = 2x^2(x-3)$

$$= 2x^3 - 6x^2$$

$$\Rightarrow f'(x) = 6x^2 - 12x = 0 \text{ at S.V.}$$

$$6x(x-2) = 0$$

$$x = 0 \; ; x = 2$$

$$f(0) = 0 \; ; \; f(2) = -8$$

x	$\rightarrow$	0	$\rightarrow$		2	$\rightarrow$
$f'(x)$	+	0	−	−	0	+
shape	↗	→	↘	↘	→	↗

Max T.P. at $(0,0)$ Min T.P at $(2,-8)$

(b)

$$-8 < k < 0$$

$\{ k > 0 \text{ and } k < -8 \text{ intersect once} \}$

Q2 (a)

Let M be the midpoint of BC, then M is the point $\left(\frac{9}{2}, \frac{5}{2}\right)$

Gradient $BC = \frac{3-2}{3-6} = \frac{-1}{3}$

$\Rightarrow$ Gradient of perpendicular bisector $= 3$ $\{$ use $m_1 \times m_2 = -1 \}$

Eqn perp. bis. is $\quad y - \frac{5}{2} = 3\left(x - \frac{9}{2}\right)$

$$y - \frac{5}{2} = 3x - \frac{27}{2}$$

$$\underline{y = 3x - 11} \qquad \{ y - 3x = -11 \}$$

(b)

Let the centre be H the point where the perpendicular bisectors meet. $y + 2x = 4$ ——①

from (a) $y - 3x = -11$ ——②

①−② $5x = 15 \Rightarrow x = 3 ; y = -2$

H is the point $(3, -2)$

Radius is AH $= \sqrt{(3-(-1))^2 + ((-2)-1)^2} = 5$

$\Rightarrow$ Eqn. is $\underline{(x-3)^2 + (y+2)^2 = 25}$ $\{ x^2 + y^2 - 6x + 4y - 12 = 0 \}$
circle

Q3
(a)

By the sine Rule

$$\frac{p}{\sin x^\circ} = \frac{r}{\sin(180-2x^\circ)}$$

$$\Rightarrow \frac{p}{\sin x^\circ} = \frac{r}{\sin 2x^\circ}$$

$$\Rightarrow \frac{\sin x^\circ}{p} = \frac{\sin 2x^\circ}{r}$$

$\triangle$ isosceles $\Rightarrow P = x^\circ$

$Q\hat{R}P = (180-2x)^\circ$

(b)
(i)

If $p = r$

Then $x^\circ = 60^\circ$ {Equilateral $\triangle$}

(ii)

If $p = r$, then $\sin x^\circ = \sin 2x^\circ$

$$\sin 2x^\circ - \sin x^\circ = 0$$
$$2\sin x^\circ \cos x^\circ - \sin x^\circ = 0$$
$$\sin x^\circ (2\cos x^\circ - 1) = 0$$
$$\sin x = 0 \quad ; \quad \cos x = \frac{1}{2}$$

{ Reject $x = 0, 180, 300$
as $0 < x < 180$ }

$$x = 60^\circ$$

Q4
(a)

$y = 2 - x$

$y = \log_{10} x$

$x \doteqdot 1.7$

38

Q4
(b) At the point of intersection, $\log_{10} x = 2 - x$

$$\Rightarrow \log_{10} x + x - 2 = 0$$

Let $f(x) = \log_{10} x + x - 2$, let the required value $= x_r$

$f(1.7) < 0$ and $f(1.8) > 0 \Rightarrow \quad 1.7 < x_r < 1.8$

$f(1.75) < 0$ and $f(1.775) > 0 \Rightarrow \quad 1.75 < x_r < 1.775$

$f(1.755) < 0$ and $f(1.765) > 0 \Rightarrow \quad 1.755 < x_r < 1.765$

$\{\text{change of sign} \Rightarrow \text{root}\} \quad \Rightarrow \underline{\underline{x_r = 1.76}} \quad$ to 2 dec. places.

Q5
(a)
(i) $\overrightarrow{VF} = \underline{f} - \underline{v} = \begin{pmatrix} 1 \\ 1 \\ -10 \end{pmatrix} \qquad \overrightarrow{VE} = \underline{e} - \underline{v} = \begin{pmatrix} 1 \\ -1 \\ -10 \end{pmatrix}$

E is the point $(2, 0, -7)$

(ii) $\cos E\hat{V}F = \dfrac{\overrightarrow{VE} \cdot \overrightarrow{VF}}{|\overrightarrow{VE}||\overrightarrow{VF}|} = \dfrac{1 \times 1 + 1 \times (-1) + (-10)(-10)}{\sqrt{102} \cdot \sqrt{102}}$

$$= \frac{100}{102}$$

$$\underline{\underline{E\hat{V}F \doteqdot 11.4°}} \qquad \{11.365°\}$$

(b) Area $\Delta = \frac{1}{2} VE \cdot VF \cdot \sin EVF$

$$= \frac{1}{2} \sqrt{102} \cdot \sqrt{102} \sin 11.4°$$

$$= 10.08$$

$$\doteqdot \underline{\underline{10 \ cm^2}}$$

Q6

$P(x) = x^3 \cos x \qquad$ let $f(x) = x^3 \qquad$ let $g(x) = \cos x$

$\qquad\qquad\qquad\qquad \Rightarrow f'(x) = 3x^2 \qquad \Rightarrow g'(x) = -\sin x$

$\Rightarrow P'(x) = 3x^2 \cos x + x^3(-\sin x)$

$$= \underline{\underline{3x^2 \cos x - x^3 \sin x}}$$

Q7
(a)

$$P_t = P_0 e^{-kt}$$

$$10 = 50 e^{-24k} \qquad \{\text{After 24 hours Pressure} = 10\}$$

$$e^{-24k} = \frac{1}{5}$$

$$-24k = \log_e\left(\frac{1}{5}\right) \qquad \{\text{Take } \log_e \text{ of both sides}\}$$

$$k = \frac{\log_e\left(\frac{1}{5}\right)}{-24}$$

$$\underline{k \doteq 0.067}$$

(b)

$$P_4 = 50 e^{-0.067 \times 4}$$

$$P_4 \doteq 38.25 \text{ units}$$

$$\left.\begin{array}{l} \text{OR} \\ \text{Solve } 30 = 50e^{-0.067t} \\ \qquad\qquad t \doteq 7.6 \text{ hours} \\ \text{So Tyre O.K. for } 3\frac{1}{2} \text{ hours} \end{array}\right\}$$

since $38.25 > 30$

The tractor could be driven a little further

Q8
(a)

Let $\cos 20t° + \sqrt{3}\sin 20t° = k\cos(20t - \alpha)°$

$$= k\cos 20t°\cos\alpha° + k\sin 20t°\sin\alpha°$$

$$\left.\begin{array}{l} k\cos\alpha = 1 \\ k\sin\alpha = \sqrt{3} \end{array}\right\} \Rightarrow k = \sqrt{(1^2 + (\sqrt{3})^2)}$$

$$\underline{k = 2}$$

$$\left.\begin{array}{l} k\sin\alpha = \sqrt{3} \\ k\cos\alpha = 1 \end{array}\right\} \Rightarrow \tan\alpha° = \sqrt{3} \qquad \underline{\alpha = 60} \qquad \underline{d = 2\cos(20t - 60)°}$$

(b)

$$d = 2\cos(20t - 60)°$$

(c)

Amplitude $= 2$
Period $= 18°$
Phase shift $= 3°$
$\Rightarrow$ Max $(3, 2)$ Min $(12, -2)$

Cuts t axis where:-
$2\cos(20t - 60)° = 0$
$20t - 60 = 90, 270°$
$20t° = 150, 330°$
$t = 7.5, 16.5$

Q8
(c)

$\text{let } d = 2\cos(20t - 60)° = 1.5$

$\cos(20t - 60)° = 0.75$

$20t° - 60° = 41.4°, 318.6°$

$20t° = 101.4°, 378.6°$

$t = 5.07, 18.93$

Hence required values are $t = 0.9$ and 5.1

$\{$ 18.9 is outwith the domain, see the graph in part (b) $\}$

Q9
(a)

If 12% per hour is lost, then 88% remain

Let A_t = the amount in units remaining t hours after
taking the antibiotic pill

Then $A_1 = 0.88 A_0$

$A_2 = 0.88 A_1 = 0.88^2 A_0$

$A_3 = 0.88 A_2 = 0.88^3 A_0$

$\Rightarrow A_t = 0.88^t A_0 \Rightarrow A_6 = 0.88^6 . 50 \quad \{6 \text{ hours}\}$

$= 23.2$ units

(b)

In this course of treatment, let U_n = the units
remaining after "n" 6 hour periods

e.g. $U_1 = 23.2 + 50 = 73.2$ can be written as

$U_1 = 0.88^6 U_0 + 50 = 73.2$

$U_2 = 0.88^6 U_1 + 50 = 84$

$U_3 = 0.88^6 U_2 + 50 = 89$

$U_4 = 0.88^6 U_3 + 50 = 91.3 \quad \{ \text{seems to be converging} \}$

$\Rightarrow U_{n+1} = 0.88^6 U_n + 50$

If this sequence converges to a limit "u"

Then $U_{n+1} = U_n = U \Rightarrow U = 0.88^6 U + 50$

$0.535 U = 50 \quad \{0.88^6 = 0.465\}$

$U \doteqdot 93.4$ units

The doctor should prescribe the treatment as the level < 100 units
during the entire course.

Q10 (a)

Since it passes through $(-20,0)$ and $(20,0)$

The equation is of the form $y = k(x+20)(x-20)$

{ $x = 20$ is a root $\Rightarrow (x-20)$ is a factor } $y = k(x^2 - 400)$

It also passes through $(0,40) \Rightarrow 40 = -400k$

$$k = -\tfrac{1}{10}$$

Hence the equation is

$$y = \frac{-1}{10}(x^2 - 400)$$

$$y = 40 - \frac{x^2}{10}$$

(b)

Let the lines AC and BC represent the frame.

$\Rightarrow A(-25,0)$ $C(0,50)$

$\Rightarrow$ gradient$_{AC}$ $= 2$; y intercept $= 50$

Eqn$_{AC}$ is $y = 2x + 50$

{ Show AC, BC are tangents }

This line meets the parabola

where $2x + 50 = 40 - \dfrac{x^2}{10}$

$20x + 500 = 400 - x^2$

$x^2 + 20x + 100 = 0$

$(x + 10)^2 = 0$

$\Rightarrow x = -10$ (twice); $y = 30$

$\Rightarrow$ tangent at $(-10, 30)$

B is the point $(25,0)$

Likewise the line BC

has gradient $= -2$

y intercept $= 50$

Eqn$_{BC}$ is $y = -2x + 50$

BC meets the parabola where:-

$40 - \dfrac{x^2}{10} = -2x + 50$

$\Rightarrow x^2 - 20x + 100 = 0$

$(x - 10)^2 = 0$

$\Rightarrow x = 10$ (twice) ; $y = 30$

$\Rightarrow$ tangent at $(10,30)$

Hence AC and BC touch the cover

Q11
(a)

let $y = f(x) = \sqrt{x} = x^{1/2}$ $\left\{ \begin{array}{l} \text{Point of contact is} \\ Q(\ ,\ ) \end{array} \right\}$

$\Rightarrow f'(x) = \frac{1}{2} x^{-1/2}$

$= \frac{1}{2\sqrt{x}}$ $\left\{ \begin{array}{l} \text{At } Q \\ m_{tangent} = m_{curve} \end{array} \right\}$

Gradient at $x=1 = f'(1) = \frac{1}{2}$ $\{ m = f'(1) \}$

Equn is $y - 1 = \frac{1}{2}(x-1)$ $\{ \text{use } y - b = m(x-a) \}$
PQ

$2y - 2 = x - 1$

$\underline{\underline{2y = x + 1}}$ At P, $x = 0 \Rightarrow y = \frac{1}{2}$

$\underline{\underline{\text{P is the point } (0, \frac{1}{2})}}$

(b)   Area OPQR $= \frac{1}{2}(1 + \frac{1}{2}) \times 1 = \frac{3}{4}$ units^2

(c)   Area $= \int_0^1 \sqrt{x}\ dx = \int_0^1 x^{1/2} dx$

$= \left[\frac{2x^{3/2}}{3} \right]_0^1$

$= \underline{\underline{\frac{2}{3} \text{ units}^2}}$

(d)   Reduction $= \frac{3}{4} - \frac{2}{3} = \frac{1}{12}$ units^2

% Reduction $= \frac{1/12}{3/4} \times 100 = \underline{\underline{11.1\%}}$

The objection seems reasonably valid

There is slightly more than a 10% reduction in space

1992 — Paper I

Q1

$$f(x) = y = 5x^3 - 6x^2 \implies f(1) = -1$$

$$f'(x) = \frac{dy}{dx} = 15x^2 - 12x \implies f'(1) = 3 \qquad \{m = f'(x)\}$$

Hence Eqn. is
$$y - (-1) = 3(x-1) \qquad \left\{\begin{matrix} use:- \\ y - b = m(x-a) \end{matrix}\right\}$$
tangent
$$y + 1 = 3x - 3$$
$$\underline{y = 3x - 4}$$

Q2

a) E is the mid point of AB $\implies$ E = (2, -1)

$$m_{CE} = \frac{8 - (-1)}{-1 - 2} = -3 \qquad \left\{\begin{matrix} use:- \\ m = \frac{y_2 - y_1}{x_2 - x_1} \end{matrix}\right\}$$

Eqn. is
$$y - 8 = -3(x - (-1)) \qquad \left\{\begin{matrix} use:- \\ y - b = m(x-a) \end{matrix}\right\}$$
CE
$$y - 8 = -3x - 3$$
$$\underline{y = -3x + 5}$$

$$m_{AC} = \frac{8 - 0}{-1 - 7} = -1 \qquad \{m_1 \times m_2 = -1\}$$

$$\implies m_{BD} = 1$$

Eqn. is
$$y - (-2) = 1(x - (-3)) \qquad \{y - b = m(x-a)\}$$
BD
$$y + 2 = x + 3$$
$$\underline{y = x + 1}$$

b) BD meets CE at J where $x + 1 = -3x + 5$ {from (a)}

$$4x = 4$$
$$x = 1$$
$$\implies \underline{y = 2} \qquad \{\text{By substitution}\}$$

Hence $\underline{J = (1, 2)}$

44

Q3

If $(x-2)$ is a factor, then $f(2) = 0$

$$\begin{array}{c|cccc} 2 & 1 & k & -4 & -12 \\ & & 2 & 2k+4 & 4k \\ \hline & 1 & k+2 & 2k & 4k-12 = 0 \end{array}$$

{ Use :- synthetic division }

$$4k = 12$$

$$\underline{\underline{k = 3}}$$

Q4

$$\frac{dy}{dx} = 3x^2 + 1$$

$$y = x^3 + x + C \qquad \{ \text{Integrate both sides} \}$$

At $(-1, 2)$; $2 = (-1)^3 + (-1) + C$

$$\Rightarrow C = 4$$

Hence $\underline{\underline{y = x^3 + x + 4}}$

Q5

$$3 \cos(2x - 40)° - 1 = 0$$

$$3 \cos(2x - 40)° = 1$$

$$\cos(2x - 40)° = \tfrac{1}{3}$$

$$2x - 40 = 70.5, \ 289.5, \ 430.5, \ 649.5$$

$$2x = 110.5, \ 329.5, \ 470.5, \ 689.5$$

$$x = 55.3, \ 164.7, \ 235.3, \ 344.7$$

Hence the required $\underline{\underline{x = 235.3}}$ $\{ 180 < x < 270 \}$

Q6

$$f(g(x)) = f\left(\tfrac{1}{x} - 2\right) = \frac{1}{\left(\tfrac{1}{x} - 2\right) + 2}$$

$$= \frac{1}{\tfrac{1}{x}}$$

$$= \underline{\underline{x}}$$

Q7
(a)

$$\sin x° - 3\cos x° = k\sin(x-\alpha)°$$
$$= k\sin x°\cos\alpha° - k\cos x°\sin\alpha°$$

$\Rightarrow k\sin\alpha° = 3$

$k\cos\alpha° = 1$

Hence (i) $k^2 = 3^2 + 1^2 = 10$ $\left\{ \sin^2\alpha° + \cos^2\alpha° = 1 \right\}$

$\Rightarrow \underline{k = \sqrt{10}}$

(ii) $\tan\alpha° = 3$ $\left\{ \dfrac{\sin\alpha°}{\cos\alpha°} = \tan\alpha° \right\}$

$\Rightarrow \underline{\alpha = 71.6}$

Hence $\underline{\sin x° - 3\cos x° = \sqrt{10}\sin(x-71.6)°}$

(b)

Max. Val. of $5 + \sin x° - 3\cos x° =$ Max.Val.of $5 + \sqrt{10}\sin(x-71.6)°$

$$= \underline{\underline{5 + \sqrt{10}}}$$

Max.Val. occurs where $(x-71.6)° = 90°$

$$\underline{\underline{x = 161.6}}$$

Q8

$$\int_1^9 \frac{x+1}{\sqrt{x}}\,dx = \int_1^9 \frac{x+1}{x^{\frac{1}{2}}}\,dx = \int_1^9 (x^{\frac{1}{2}} + x^{-\frac{1}{2}})\,dx \qquad *$$

$$= \left[\frac{2}{3}x^{\frac{3}{2}} + 2x^{\frac{1}{2}} \right]_1^9$$

$$= \left(\frac{2}{3}(9)^{\frac{3}{2}} + 2(9)^{\frac{1}{2}} \right) - \left(\frac{2}{3}(1)^{\frac{3}{2}} + 2(1)^{\frac{1}{2}} \right)$$

$$= (18 + 6) - \left(\frac{2}{3} + 2 \right)$$

$$= \underline{\underline{21\tfrac{1}{3}}}$$

* N.B. A useful rule is A.B.C.

                 = Algebra Before Calculus

Q9

Centre $(4,3)$ Let $S = (4,3)$

radius $= \sqrt{(16+9-21)}$

$= 2$ units

$$\begin{cases} \text{If } x^2 + y^2 + 2gx + 2fy + c = 0 \\ \text{Then (i) centre is } (-g, -f) \\ \quad\quad \text{(ii) radius } = \sqrt{(g^2 + f^2 - c)} \end{cases}$$

$OS^2 = 4^2 + 3^2 = 25$

$\underline{OS = 5 \text{ units}}$

Required Distance $= 5 - 2 = 3$ units

$\underline{\underline{= 45m}}$

Q10

(a)

$y = g(x)$

(b)

$y = -2g(x)$

47

Q11

$$f(x) = 2x^{3/2} + \sin^2 x \qquad \{ \sin^2 x = (\sin x)^2 \}$$

$$f'(x) = \tfrac{3}{2} 2x^{1/2} + 2(\sin x)\cos x \qquad \{ \text{use the chain rule} \}$$

$$= \underline{3x^{1/2} + 2\sin x \cos x}$$

$$\text{or} \quad \underline{3\sqrt{x} + \sin 2x} \qquad \{ \text{simplifying} \}$$

Q12

Since $y = \log_{10}(x+a)$ passes through $(-2, 0)$

Then $(-2 + a) = 1$

$\Rightarrow \underline{a = 3}$

$$\left\{ \begin{array}{l} \text{i.e } \log_{10}(x+a) = 0 \\ \Rightarrow \quad x + a = 1 \\ \text{since } \log_{10} 1 = 0 \end{array} \right\}$$

Q13

Since OABC is a kite, then $\angle COB = \angle BOA$

$$\Rightarrow \underline{\angle COA = 2\angle BOA}$$

In $\triangle AOB \qquad \tan BOA = 3/4 = 0.75$

$$\Rightarrow \underline{\angle BOA = 36.870°} \qquad (36.87)$$

$$\Rightarrow \underline{\angle COA = 73.740°} \qquad (73.74)$$

Gradient of OC $= \tan COA = 3.429 \qquad (3.43)$

$$\doteqdot \underline{3.43} \qquad (2\,\text{d.p.})$$

Q14

(a)

$$\int_0^{\pi/2} \cos 2x \, dx = \left[\tfrac{1}{2} \sin 2x \right]_0^{\pi/2} = \tfrac{1}{2}(\sin \pi) - \tfrac{1}{2}(\sin 0)$$

$$= \underline{\underline{0}}$$

(b)

$y = \cos 2x$

The positive and negative areas cancel each other out.

Q15

$$\vec{AB} = \underline{b} - \underline{a} = \begin{pmatrix} 3 \\ 1 \\ -2 \end{pmatrix} - \begin{pmatrix} -1 \\ 3 \\ 4 \end{pmatrix} = \begin{pmatrix} 4 \\ -2 \\ -6 \end{pmatrix} \Rightarrow \vec{BC} = \tfrac{1}{2}\vec{AB} = \begin{pmatrix} 2 \\ -1 \\ -3 \end{pmatrix}$$

$$\vec{BC} = \underline{c} - \underline{b} = \begin{pmatrix} 2 \\ -1 \\ -3 \end{pmatrix}$$

$$\underline{c} = \begin{pmatrix} 2 \\ -1 \\ -3 \end{pmatrix} + \underline{b} \Rightarrow \underline{c} = \begin{pmatrix} 5 \\ 0 \\ -5 \end{pmatrix} ; \quad C = (5, 0, -5)$$

Q16

Circle centre $(2,2)$; radius $= 5$

By Dist. Formula $AC^2 = (10-2)^2 + (8-2)^2 = 100$

$\Rightarrow AC = 10$

$$\left\{ \begin{array}{l} \text{If } (x-a)^2 + (y-b)^2 = r^2 \\ \text{Then (i) centre is } (a,b) \\ \quad \text{(ii) radius } = r \end{array} \right\}$$

In $\triangle ABC$, By Pythagoras $AB = \sqrt{75}$

Hence Area $ABC = \tfrac{1}{2} \cdot 5 \cdot \sqrt{75}$

$= \dfrac{25\sqrt{3}}{2}$ un^2

$\{ \sqrt{75} = 5\sqrt{3} \}$

$\{ \text{Area} \doteq 21.65 \text{un}^2 \}$

Q17

Let $kx^2 - 8x + k = 0$

For NO REAL ROOTS $64 - 4k^2 < 0$ $\qquad \{ b^2 - 4ac < 0 \}$

$\qquad 4k^2 > 64$

$\qquad k^2 > 16$

$\qquad k > 4$ $\qquad$ Hence $k = 5$ $\qquad \{ k > 0 \}$

Q18

$$\underline{a} \cdot (\underline{a} + \underline{b}) = \underline{a} \cdot \underline{a} + \underline{a} \cdot \underline{b} = |\underline{a}||\underline{a}|\cos 0° + |\underline{a}||\underline{b}|\cos 60°$$

$$= 2 \times 2 \times 1 \quad + \quad 2 \times 3 \times \tfrac{1}{2}$$

$$= 7$$

Q19

$m = f'(x) = 1$, at $x = 0$; i.e $f'(0) = 1$

$m = f'(x) = 0$, at $x = a$; i.e. $f'(a) = 0$

$m = f'(x) = -1$ at $x = 2a$, i.e $f'(2a) = -1$

Since $f(x)$ is quadratic

Then $f'(x)$ is linear

Q1
(a)

$f(x) = x^3 + x^2 - 16x - 16$ { Use synthetic division / Try factors of 16 }

$$
\begin{array}{r|rrrr}
-1 & 1 & 1 & -16 & -16 \\
   &   & -1 & 0 & 16 \\
\hline
4 & 1 & 0 & -16 & 0 \quad \Rightarrow (x+1) \text{ is a factor} \\
  &   & 4 & 16 & \\
\hline
  & 1 & 4 & 0 & \quad \Rightarrow (x-4) \text{ is a factor}
\end{array}
$$

$(x + 4)$ is a factor

Hence $f(x) = (x+4)(x+1)(x-4)$

(b)   Curve crosses y-axis at $x = 0$; $f(0) = -16 \Rightarrow$ <u>Pt $(0, -16)$</u>

curve crosses x-axis at $y = 0$; $f(x) = 0$

$$\Rightarrow (x+4)(x+1)(x-4) = 0$$

$$x = -4, -1, 4$$

$$\Rightarrow \underline{\text{Pts } (-4,0), (-1,0), (4,0)}$$

(c) $f(x) = x^3 + x^2 - 16x - 16$

$f'(x) = 3x^2 + 2x - 16 = 0$ at S.V.

$(3x + 8)(x - 2) = 0$

$3x + 8 = 0$ or $x - 2 = 0$

$x = -\dfrac{8}{3}$; $x = 2$

$f\left(-\dfrac{8}{3}\right) = \dfrac{400}{27}$; $f(2) = -36$

Table of Values

x	$\rightarrow$	$-\frac{8}{3}$	$\rightarrow$		$\rightarrow$	2	$\rightarrow$
$f'(x)$	+	0	−		−	0	+
Shape	↗	→	↘		↘	→	↗

Max T.P. at $\underline{\left(-\dfrac{8}{3}, \dfrac{400}{27}\right)}$ Min T.P. at $\underline{\left(2, -36\right)}$

Q2
(a)

By the distance formula $|\overrightarrow{BR}|^2 = (7-5)^2 + (2-(-5))^2 + (3-(-1))^2$

$$= 4 + 49 + 16 = 69$$

Hence $|\overrightarrow{BR}| = \sqrt{69}$ un $\Rightarrow$ <u>Distance $= 2\sqrt{69}$ km</u>

(b)

$|\overrightarrow{MR}|^2 = (7-(-2))^2 + (2-4)^2 + (3-8.5)^2$

$$= 81 + 4 + 30.25 = 115.25$$

$|\overrightarrow{MR}| = \sqrt{115.25} \Rightarrow$ Distance $= 2\sqrt{115.25}$ km

Q 2 (b)
cont.

$$\text{Speed} = \frac{\text{Distance}}{\text{Time}} = \frac{2\sqrt{115 \cdot 25}}{3/60} = 429 \cdot 42$$

$$\doteqdot \quad 429 \text{ km}/\text{hr}$$

(c)

$$\vec{TC} = \underline{c} - \underline{t} = \begin{pmatrix} 12 \\ -4 \\ 1 \end{pmatrix} - \begin{pmatrix} 0 \\ 0 \\ 0 \end{pmatrix} = \begin{pmatrix} 12 \\ -4 \\ 1 \end{pmatrix}$$

$$\vec{BR} = \underline{r} - \underline{b} = \begin{pmatrix} 7 \\ 2 \\ 3 \end{pmatrix} - \begin{pmatrix} 5 \\ -5 \\ -1 \end{pmatrix} = \begin{pmatrix} 2 \\ 7 \\ 4 \end{pmatrix}$$

$$\vec{TC} \cdot \vec{BR} = \begin{pmatrix} 12 \\ -4 \\ 1 \end{pmatrix} \cdot \begin{pmatrix} 2 \\ 7 \\ 4 \end{pmatrix} = 12 \times 2 + (-4) \times 7 + 1 \times 4 = 0$$

$\Rightarrow$ TC is perpendicular to BR (since $\vec{TC} \cdot \vec{BR} = 0$)

(d) Let $\angle TCR = \theta°$; Then $\cos\theta° = \dfrac{\vec{CT} \cdot \vec{CR}}{|\vec{CT}||\vec{CR}|}$ $\qquad \left\{ \vec{CR} = \begin{pmatrix} -5 \\ 6 \\ 2 \end{pmatrix} \right\}$

$$= \frac{\begin{pmatrix} -12 \\ 4 \\ -1 \end{pmatrix} \cdot \begin{pmatrix} -5 \\ 6 \\ 2 \end{pmatrix}}{\sqrt{161} \ \sqrt{65}} \qquad \left\{ \frac{82}{102 \cdot 3} \right\}$$

$$= 0 \cdot 802$$

$$\Rightarrow \quad \underline{\theta = 36 \cdot 7} \qquad \text{Hence} \underline{\angle TCR = 36 \cdot 7°}$$

Q3

(a) 40% Removed $\Rightarrow$ 60% Remain
Let the level after n weeks $= U_n$ mg/l $\qquad (U_0 = 0)$

After n weeks $\quad U_n = 0 \cdot 6 \, U_{n-1} + 2 \cdot 5 \quad (U_4 = 5 \cdot 44)$

If a fixed value "U" is reached then $U = 0 \cdot 6 \, U + 2 \cdot 5$

$$0 \cdot 4 U = 2 \cdot 5$$

$$\text{limit} \quad \underline{U = 6 \cdot 25 \Rightarrow \text{Danger}}$$

(b) 30% clean $\Rightarrow$ 70% Remain
70% of $2 \cdot 5 = 1 \cdot 75$

Now $\quad U_n = 0 \cdot 6 \, U_{n-1} + 1 \cdot 75$

If a fixed value "U" is reached then $U = 0 \cdot 6 U + 1 \cdot 75$

$$0 \cdot 4 U = 1 \cdot 75$$

$$\text{limit} \quad \underline{U = 4 \cdot 375 \Rightarrow \text{Safe}}$$

Hence; $\underline{\text{YES}}$ the L.A. should grant permission

Q4
(a)

$$m_t = m_0 e^{-0.02t} \Rightarrow m_{10} = 500 e^{-0.02 \times 10}$$
$$= 409.37 g$$

(b)

$$m = 500 e^{-0.02t} = 250$$
$$e^{-0.02t} = 0.5$$

$$-0.02t \ln e = \ln 0.5 \qquad \left\{ \begin{array}{c} \text{Take } \log_e \text{ of} \\ \text{both sides} \end{array} \right\}$$

$$t = \frac{\ln 0.5}{-0.02} \qquad \left\{ \ln = \log_e \right\}$$

$$t = 34.66$$

Hence the half-life $\doteq$ <u>34.7 years</u>

(c)

Q5
(a)

Volume = Area of base × height

$$500 = . \quad x^2 \times h$$
$$\Rightarrow h = \underline{\frac{500}{x^2}} \quad m$$

Area of Netting required $= x^2 + 4 \times h \times x \qquad \{ \text{TOP} + 4 \text{ SIDES} \}$

$$= x^2 + 4 \times \frac{500}{x^2} \times x$$

$$= \underline{\underline{x^2 + \frac{2000}{x}}} \quad m^2$$

Q5
(b)

$A(x) = x^2 + \dfrac{2000}{x}$

$\qquad = x^2 + 200 x^{-1}$

$A'(x) = 2x - 2000 x^{-2} = 0$ at S.V.

$\qquad 2x - \dfrac{2000}{x^2} = 0$

$\qquad 2x^3 - 2000 = 0$

$\qquad x^3 - 1000 = 0$

$\qquad x = 10$

Table of Values			
x	$\rightarrow$	10	$\rightarrow$
$A'(x)$	$-$	0	$+$
shape	↘	$\rightarrow$	↗

Min T.P.
at $(10, 300)$

$h = \dfrac{500}{x^2} = 5 \qquad A(10) = 300$

Hence required dimensions are $\underline{\underline{10m \text{ by } 10m \text{ by } 5m}}$

Q6
(a)

$\underline{a} = \begin{pmatrix} 4 \\ 1 \\ 0 \end{pmatrix} - \begin{pmatrix} 3 \\ -1 \\ 2 \end{pmatrix} = \underline{\underline{\begin{pmatrix} 1 \\ 2 \\ -2 \end{pmatrix}}} \quad ; \quad \underline{b} = \begin{pmatrix} 2 \\ 1 \\ 1 \end{pmatrix} - \begin{pmatrix} 3 \\ -1 \\ 2 \end{pmatrix} = \underline{\underline{\begin{pmatrix} -1 \\ 2 \\ -1 \end{pmatrix}}}$

$\underline{c} = \underline{a} \times \underline{b} = \begin{bmatrix} 2 \times (-1) - (-2) \times 2 \\ (-2) \times (-1) - 1 \times (-1) \\ 1 \times 2 - 2 \times (-1) \end{bmatrix} = \underline{\underline{\begin{pmatrix} 2 \\ 3 \\ 4 \end{pmatrix}}}$

(b)

$\underline{a} \cdot \underline{c} = \begin{pmatrix} 1 \\ 2 \\ -2 \end{pmatrix} \cdot \begin{pmatrix} 2 \\ 3 \\ 4 \end{pmatrix} = 2 + 6 - 8 = \underline{0} \quad \Rightarrow \underline{c}$ is perpendicular to $\underline{a}$

$\underline{b} \cdot \underline{c} = \begin{pmatrix} -1 \\ 2 \\ -1 \end{pmatrix} \cdot \begin{pmatrix} 2 \\ 3 \\ 4 \end{pmatrix} = -2 + 6 - 4 = \underline{0} \quad \Rightarrow \underline{c}$ is perpendicular to $\underline{b}$

$\underline{c}$ is perpendicular to both $\underline{a}$ and $\underline{b}$ $\Rightarrow$ $\underline{c}$ is perpendicular to the plane
of $\underline{a}$ and $\underline{b}$

Q7
(a)

$\qquad\qquad 3 \sin 2x° = 2 \sin x°$

$\qquad 3 \sin 2x - 2 \sin x° = 0 \qquad\qquad \{\sin 2x° = 2 \sin x° \cos x°\}$

$3 . 2 \sin x° \cos x° - 2 \sin x° = 0$

$\qquad 2 \sin x° (3 \cos x° - 1) = 0$

$\qquad 2 \sin x° = 0 \quad$ or $\quad 3 \cos x° - 1 = 0$

$\qquad \sin x° = 0 \qquad\qquad \cos x° = \tfrac{1}{3}$

$\qquad x = 0, 180, 360 \qquad x = 70.5, 289.5$

Hence $\underline{x = 0, 70.5, 180, 289.5, 360}$

Q7

(b) $f(x) = 2 \sin x°$; $g(x) = 3 \sin 2x°$

(c) from (a) $\underline{A = (70.5, 1.89)}$ and $\underline{B = (289.5, -1.89)}$

(d) $3 \sin 2x° < 2 \sin x°$ where $g(x) < f(x)$ $\qquad \{ f(70.5) = 1.89 \text{ etc...} \}$

$\Rightarrow \underline{\underline{\text{where } 70.5 < x < 180 \text{ AND } 289.5 < x < 360}}$

Q8

(a) Let the perpendicular from L meet AB at P

Hence $\angle PBL = 180 - b°$ $\Rightarrow$ $\tan PBL = -\tan b°$

In $\triangle BLP$, $\tan B = \dfrac{d}{BP}$

$\Rightarrow BP = \dfrac{d}{\tan B}$

$\Rightarrow \underline{BP = \dfrac{-d}{\tan b°}}$

In $\triangle ALP$, $\tan A = \dfrac{d}{AP}$

$\Rightarrow \underline{AP = \dfrac{d}{\tan a°}}$

$AB = AP + PB$

$= \underline{\dfrac{d}{\tan a°} - \dfrac{d}{\tan b°}}$

(b) $AB = \dfrac{d}{\tan a°} - \dfrac{d}{\tan b°}$ $= \dfrac{d}{\frac{\sin a°}{\cos a°}} - \dfrac{d}{\frac{\sin b°}{\cos b°}}$ $\qquad \left\{ \tan a° = \dfrac{\sin a°}{\cos a°} \right\}$

$= \dfrac{d \frac{\sin b°}{\cos b°} - d \frac{\sin a°}{\cos a°}}{\frac{\sin a°}{\cos a°} \cdot \frac{\sin b°}{\cos b°}}$ $\qquad \left\{ \times \dfrac{\cos a° \cdot \cos b°}{\cos a° \cos b°} \right\}$

$= \dfrac{d \sin b° \cos a° - d \cos b° \sin a°}{\sin a° \sin b°}$

$= \dfrac{d \sin(b - a)°}{\underline{\sin a° \sin b°}}$

54

Q8 (c)

from (b) $AB = \dfrac{d \sin (135-60)^\circ}{\sin 60^\circ \sin 135^\circ} = 14$

$\Rightarrow \quad d = \dfrac{14 \sin 60^\circ \sin 135^\circ}{\sin 75^\circ}$

$d = 8.876$

Hence the shortest distance $\doteq$ 9 miles

Q9 (a)

$A = (0,-50)$; $m_{PB} = m_{AB} = \dfrac{4}{3}$ $\qquad \left\{ \vec{AB} = \begin{pmatrix} 3 \\ 4 \end{pmatrix} \right\}$

Eqn$_{PB}$ is $\underline{y = \dfrac{4}{3}x - 50}$ $\qquad\qquad\qquad \{ y = mx + c \}$

(b) Eqn$_{CIRCle}$ is $\underline{x^2 + y^2 = 900}$ $\qquad\qquad \{ x^2 + y^2 = r^2 \}$

(c)

$y = \dfrac{4}{3}x - 50 \Rightarrow y^2 = \dfrac{16}{9}x^2 - \dfrac{400}{3}x + 2500$

$x^2 + y^2 = 900 \Rightarrow x^2 + \dfrac{16}{9}x^2 - \dfrac{400}{3}x + 2500 = 900$

$9x^2 + 16x^2 - 1200x + 14400 = 0$

$25x^2 - 1200x + 14400 = 0$

$x^2 - 48x + 576 = 0$

$(x - 24)^2 = 0$

$x = 24$ (twice)

Equal Roots $\Rightarrow$ tangent at $x = 24$ where $y = -18$

Hence $\underline{P = (24, -18)}$

Q10 (a)

$\text{Area} = \displaystyle\int_0^2 (2x - x^2)\, dx = \left[x^2 - \dfrac{x^3}{3} \right]_0^2 = 4 - \dfrac{8}{3} = \dfrac{4}{3} \text{ un}^2$

(b)

$\text{Area} = \dfrac{1}{2} \cdot P \times \dfrac{1}{2}P = \dfrac{4}{3}$ $\qquad \{ \text{same area as (a)} \}$

$\Rightarrow \dfrac{P^2}{4} = \dfrac{4}{3}$

$P^2 = \dfrac{16}{3}$

$P = \dfrac{4}{\sqrt{3}}$

$P \doteq 2.3 \text{ un}$

$$\text{Area} = \int_{\pi/4}^{q} (\sin x - \cos x)\, dx \qquad = \frac{4}{3} \qquad \{\text{same area as (a)}\}$$

$$\Rightarrow \quad \Big[-\cos x - \sin x\Big]_{\pi/4}^{q} \qquad = \frac{4}{3}$$

$$\Rightarrow \left(-\cos q - \sin q\right) - \left(-\cos \tfrac{\pi}{4} - \sin \tfrac{\pi}{4}\right) = \frac{4}{3}$$

$$\Rightarrow -\left(\cos q + \sin q\right) + \left(\frac{1}{\sqrt{2}} + \frac{1}{\sqrt{2}}\right) = \frac{4}{3}$$

$$\Rightarrow \cos q + \sin q = \frac{2}{\sqrt{2}} - \frac{4}{3} \qquad \left\{\frac{2}{\sqrt{2}} = \sqrt{2}\right\}$$

$$\Rightarrow \underline{\underline{\cos q + \sin q = 0.081}} \qquad \{1.414 - 1.333\}$$

Let $\cos q + \sin q = R\cos(q - d)$

$$R^2 = 1^2 + 1^2 = 2 \quad ; \quad \tan d = \frac{1}{1}$$
$$\Rightarrow \underline{\underline{R = \sqrt{2}}} \qquad\qquad \underline{\underline{d = \tfrac{\pi}{4}}}$$

Hence $\cos q + \sin q = \sqrt{2}\cos\left(q - \tfrac{\pi}{4}\right) = 0.081$

$$\cos\left(q - \tfrac{\pi}{4}\right) = 0.0573$$
$$q - \tfrac{\pi}{4} = 1.5135 \qquad \{\text{Radians}\}$$
$$q = 1.5135 + \tfrac{\pi}{4}$$
$$q = 2.299$$
$$\underline{q \doteqdot 2.3}$$

N.B. (i) A graphic calculator may be helpful in :-
   PI   Qs 1, 2, 5, 7, 10 and 12 ; PII Qs 1, 3, 4 and 7
   (ii) In Q8(b) of PII it may be easier to start with
        the R.H.S, expand, divide and work backwards.
   (iii) In Q10(c) of PI, the last part (worth about 5 marks)
         could have been attempted first. (i.e. "hence..etc...")

Q1
(a)
$$\overrightarrow{AB} = \underline{b} - \underline{a} = \begin{pmatrix} -1 \\ 3 \\ 2 \end{pmatrix} - \begin{pmatrix} -3 \\ 2 \\ 4 \end{pmatrix} = \begin{pmatrix} 2 \\ 1 \\ -2 \end{pmatrix}$$

(b)
$$|\overrightarrow{AB}| = \sqrt{(2^2 + 1^2 + (-2)^2)} = \sqrt{9} = 3 \text{ units}$$

Q2
(a)

If A is the point $(-2, 3)$, then $m_{OA} = \dfrac{3}{-2}$ $\left\{ m = \dfrac{y_2 - y_1}{x_2 - x_1} \right\}$

$\Rightarrow m_{NR} = \dfrac{2}{3}$ $\left\{ m_1 \times m_2 = -1 \right\}$

Eqn$_{NR}$ is $y - 3 = \dfrac{2}{3}(x - (-2))$ $\left\{ y - b = m(x - a) \right\}$

$$3y - 9 = 2x + 4$$
$$\underline{3y = 2x + 13}$$

(b)

At $B(-5, 1)$; $\left. \begin{array}{l} 3y = 3(1) = 3 \\ 2x + 13 = 2(-5) + 13 = 3 \end{array} \right\}$ $\Rightarrow (-5, 1)$ satisfies the Eqn

$\Rightarrow \underline{(-5, 1) \text{ lies on the line } NR}$

Q3

$2x^2 + 4x + k = 0$; FOR REAL ROOTS $b^2 - 4ac \geqslant 0$

Here $\left\{ \begin{array}{l} a = 2 \\ b = 4 \\ c = k \end{array} \right\} \Rightarrow b^2 - 4ac = \begin{array}{ll} 16 - 4(2)(k) & \geqslant 0 \\ 16 - 8k & \geqslant 0 \\ -8k & \geqslant -16 \\ \underline{\underline{k \leqslant 2}} \end{array}$

Q4

"parallel to the x-axis" $\Rightarrow$ gradient $= 0 \Rightarrow f'(x) = 0$

Let $y = f(x) = 2x^3 - 3x^2 - 12x + 20$

$\Rightarrow f'(x) = 6x^2 - 6x - 12 = 0$ when $m = 0$

$$x^2 - x - 2 = 0$$
$$(x + 1)(x - 2) = 0$$
$$x + 1 = 0 \quad \text{OR} \quad x - 2 = 0$$
$$\underline{\underline{x = -1}} \quad \text{OR} \quad \underline{\underline{x = 2}}$$

25

(a) Centre of circle A is $(2,2)$ => Box Width = 4 units

Radius of circle A is 2 units => Radius of Circle B = 2 units

$\overrightarrow{AB}$ = 2 boxes along = 8 units along = $\begin{pmatrix} 8 \\ 4 \end{pmatrix}$
       1 box up   4 units up

$\overrightarrow{AB}$ = $\underline{b} - \underline{a}$ = $\begin{pmatrix} 8 \\ 4 \end{pmatrix}$ { use TRANSLATIONS Like 2 D.Vectors }

$\underline{b} - \begin{pmatrix} 2 \\ 2 \end{pmatrix} = \begin{pmatrix} 8 \\ 4 \end{pmatrix}$

$\underline{b}$ = $\begin{pmatrix} 10 \\ 6 \end{pmatrix}$ => Centre of Circle at B is $(10, 6)$

(b) Eqn of Circle at B is $(x-10)^2 + (y-6)^2 = 4$ $\{ (x-a)^2 + (y-b)^2 = r^2 \}$

26

$\sin(P+Q) = \sin P \cos Q + \cos P \sin Q$

$= \dfrac{12}{13} \cdot \dfrac{4}{5} + \dfrac{5}{13} \cdot \dfrac{3}{5}$

$= \dfrac{48}{65} + \dfrac{15}{65}$

$= \dfrac{63}{65}$

5 ← { By Pythagoras }

Q7

If $x = -3$ is a ROOT, then $f(-3) = 0$

$2x^3 - 3x^2 + px + 30$

$\begin{array}{r|rrrr} -3 & 2 & -3 & p & 30 \\ & & -6 & 27 & -3p-81 \\ \hline & 2 & -9 & p+27 & -3p-51 \end{array}$ = 0 => 3p = -51

                                    p = -17   { p+27 = 10 }

$2x^2 - 9x + 10$

$\begin{array}{r|rrr} 2 & 2 & -9 & 10 \\ & & 4 & -10 \\ \hline & 2 & -5 & 0 \end{array}$ => $(x-2)$ is a factor => $x = 2$ is a root

=> $(2x - 5)$ is a factor => $x = \dfrac{5}{2}$ is a root

Q8

$f(x) \rightarrow -f(x) + 2$

The graph of $y = f(x)$

is given a REFLECTION in Ox

followed by a TRANSLATION $\begin{pmatrix} 0 \\ 2 \end{pmatrix}$

Q9

Let $f(x) = 4\sqrt{x} + 3\cos 2x = 4x^{\frac{1}{2}} + 3\cos 2x$

$\Rightarrow f'(x) = \frac{1}{2} \cdot 4x^{-\frac{1}{2}} + 3(-\sin 2x) \cdot 2$

$= 2x^{-\frac{1}{2}} - 6\sin 2x$

$\left\{ \text{OR } \dfrac{2}{\sqrt{x}} - 6\sin 2x \right\}$

Q10

(a) gradient $= \tan\theta°$

$y = 2x + 4 \Rightarrow m_1 = \tan a° = 2$

$a = 63.4$

$x + y = 13$

$y = -x + 13$

$\Rightarrow m_2 = \tan b° = -1$

$b = 135$

(b) The required angle $= b° - a°$

$= 135° - 63.4°$

$= 71.6°$

$\left\{ \text{OR } 63.4° + 45° + \theta° = 180° \right.$
$\left. \Rightarrow \theta = 71.6 \right\}$

Q11

$g(x) = 3x + 4$

$g(0) = 4 \Rightarrow A(0,4)$ lies on $f(x)$ and $f(0) = 4$

$f'(x) = 2x - 3$

$f(x) = \int (2x - 3)\,dx = x^2 - 3x + C$ $\left\{ \text{Integrate and find C} \right\}$

$f(0) = C = 4$

Hence $f(x) = x^2 - 3x + 4$

Q12

(a)
$$\underline{a} = \begin{pmatrix} 2 \\ 0 \\ -1 \end{pmatrix} ; \quad \underline{b} = \begin{pmatrix} 1 \\ 2 \\ 1 \end{pmatrix} ; \quad \underline{c} = \begin{pmatrix} 0 \\ -1 \\ 1 \end{pmatrix}$$

Hence $\underline{a} \cdot \underline{b} + \underline{a} \cdot \underline{c} = \begin{pmatrix} 2 \\ 0 \\ -1 \end{pmatrix} \cdot \begin{pmatrix} 1 \\ 2 \\ 1 \end{pmatrix} + \begin{pmatrix} 2 \\ 0 \\ -1 \end{pmatrix} \cdot \begin{pmatrix} 0 \\ -1 \\ 1 \end{pmatrix}$

$= (2 \times 1) + 0 \times 2 + (-1) \times 1 + 2 \times 0 + 0 \times (-1) + (-1) \times 1$

$= 2 + 0 - 1 \quad + 0 + 0 - 1$

$= \underline{\underline{0}}$

(b) Since $\underline{a} \cdot \underline{b} + \underline{a} \cdot \underline{c} = \underline{a}(\underline{b} + \underline{c}) = 0$

Then $(\underline{b} + \underline{c})$ is PERPENDICULAR to $\underline{a}$

Q13

(a) $k(x) = f(g(x)) = f(3 - 2x) = 2(3 - 2x) - 1 = 6 - 4x - 1 = \underline{\underline{5 - 4x}}$

(b) $h(k(x)) = h(5 - 4x) = \frac{1}{4}(5 - (5 - 4x)) = \frac{1}{4}(4x) = \underline{\underline{x}}$

(c) Since $h(k(x)) = x$

Then $h = k^{-1}(x)$ ie. h and k are <u>INVERSES</u> of each other

Q14

$f(x)$ cubic

$\Rightarrow f'(x)$ quadratic

$y = f'(x)$ {Parabolic graph}

$f'(x)$ has roots

at $x = -2$ and 3

min T.P. at $x = \frac{1}{2}$

{y-intercept approx. $y \doteq -1$}

Q15

(a) y-intercept $= 5$; At $x = 0$, $y = a.1 \Rightarrow \underline{\underline{a = 5}}$ {$e^0 = 1$}

At $x = 3$, $y = 5e^{3k} = 20$

$e^{3k} = 4$

$3k = \ln 4$ {$\ln e = 1$}

$\underline{\underline{k = 0.462}}$

Q 15
(b)

From (a) $y = 5 e^{0.462 x}$ for $0 \leqslant x \leqslant 3$

Hence $y = 5 e^{0.462 (x-3)}$ for $3 \leqslant x \leqslant 6$

$$\left\{ \text{Translation} \begin{pmatrix} 3 \\ 0 \end{pmatrix} \right\}$$

Q 16

$$\int \sqrt{1+3x} \; dx = \int (1+3x)^{1/2} \, dx$$

$$= \frac{2(1+3x)^{3/2}}{3(3)} + C$$

$$= \frac{2}{9} (1+3x)^{3/2} + C$$

Hence $\int_0^1 \sqrt{1+3x} \, dx = \left[\frac{2}{9} (1+3x)^{3/2} \right]_0^1$

$$= \frac{2}{9} \left((4)^{3/2} - (1)^{3/2} \right) \qquad \left\{ 4^{3/2} = 8 ; \; 1^{3/2} = 1 \right\}$$

$$= \frac{2}{9} (7)$$

$$= \frac{14}{9}$$

Q 17

$f(a) = 6 \sin^2 a - \cos a = 6(1 - \cos^2 a) - \cos a \qquad \left\{ \sin^2 a = 1 - \cos^2 a \right\}$

$$= 6 - 6 \cos^2 a - \cos a$$

$$\Rightarrow f(a) = -6 \cos^2 a - \cos a + 6 \qquad \left\{ \begin{array}{l} p = -6 \\ q = -1 \\ r = 6 \end{array} \right\}$$

Hence $6 \sin^2 a - \cos a = 5$

$\Rightarrow -6 \cos^2 a - \cos a + 6 = 5$

$-6 \cos^2 a - \cos a + 1 = 0$

$6 \cos^2 a + \cos a - 1 = 0$

$(3 \cos a - 1)(2 \cos a + 1) = 0$

$3 \cos a = 1$ OR $2 \cos a = -1$

$\cos a = \frac{1}{3}$ OR $\cos a = -\frac{1}{2}$ $\qquad \{ \text{use radians} \}$

$a = 1.231$ OR $a = 2.094$ $\qquad \left\{ \text{or } \frac{2\pi}{3} \right\}$

18

The general equation of a circle is $x^2 + y^2 + 2gx + 2fy + c = 0$ $\quad \left\{ \begin{array}{l} g = 1 \\ f = \frac{3}{2} \\ c = 5 \end{array} \right\}$

Here the radius $= \sqrt{(g^2 + f^2 - c)} = \sqrt{(1 + \frac{9}{4} - 5)} = \sqrt{(-\frac{7}{4})}$

Hence the radius is <u>NOT REAL</u> $\Rightarrow$ Eqn is NOT a circle $\qquad \{ \sqrt{(-ve)} \notin R \}$

Q19

(a) LHS $= (\cos x + \sin x)^2$

$$= \cos^2 x + 2\sin x \cos x + \sin^2 x$$

$$= \underline{1 + \sin 2x} \quad = \text{RHS}$$

$$\left\{ \begin{array}{l} \cos^2 x + \sin^2 x = 1 \\ 2\sin x \cos x = \sin 2x \end{array} \right\}$$

(b) $\int (\cos x + \sin x)^2 \, dx = \int (1 + \sin 2x) \, dx$

$$= \underline{\underline{x - \tfrac{1}{2} \cos 2x + c}}$$

Q20

At $P(p, k)$, $k = \log_e p$; At $Q(q, k)$, $k = \tfrac{1}{2} \log_e q$

Hence $\log_e p = \tfrac{1}{2} \log_e q$

$\log_e p = \log_e q^{\frac{1}{2}}$

$\quad\Rightarrow\quad p = q^{\frac{1}{2}}$

$\left\{ x \log a = \log a^x \right\}$

$\quad\Rightarrow\quad \underline{\underline{p = \sqrt{q}}} \quad \text{or} \quad \underline{\underline{q = p^2}}$

if $p = 5$ then $q = 5^2 \;\underline{\underline{= 25}}$

Q21

$$f(x) = \frac{1}{x+1} = (x+1)^{-1} \qquad x \neq -1$$

$$\Rightarrow \quad f'(x) = -1(x+1)^{-2} = \frac{-1}{(x+1)^2} \qquad x \neq -1$$

Since $(x+1)^2 > 0 \Rightarrow f'(x) < 0 \qquad x \neq -1$

$\underline{\text{Hence } f(x) \text{ is DECREASING for all } x} \qquad x \neq -1$

$$\left\{ \begin{array}{l} f'(x) < 0 \Rightarrow f(x) \text{ decreasing} \\ f(x) \text{ and } f'(x) \text{ undefined at } x = -1 \end{array} \right\}$$

$f(x) = x^4 - 2x^3 + 2x - 1$ $\qquad \left\{ f(x) = (x+1)(x-1)^3 \right\}$

$f'(x) = 4x^3 - 6x^2 + 2 = 0 \quad$ at St. Val. $\left\{ \text{For St.Vs put } f'(x) = 0 \right\}$

$\qquad 2x^3 - 3x^2 + 1 = 0 \qquad \left\{ \begin{array}{l} \text{Use synthetic division} \\ \text{to factorise } f'(x) \end{array} \right\}$

$$
\begin{array}{r|rrrr}
1 & 2 & -3 & 0 & 1 \\
 & & 2 & -1 & -1 \\
\hline
1 & 2 & -1 & -1 & 0 \end{array} \Rightarrow (x-1) \text{ is a factor}
$$

$$
\begin{array}{r|rrr}
 & & 2 & 1 \\
\hline
 & 2 & 1 & 0 \end{array} \Rightarrow (x-1) \text{ is a factor}
$$

$\Rightarrow (2x+1)$ is a factor

Hence $f'(x) = (2x+1)(x-1)(x-1) = 0$ at St. Val

$\qquad 2x+1 = 0 \qquad$ OR $\qquad x - 1 = 0$

$\qquad \Rightarrow \underline{\underline{x = -\tfrac{1}{2}}} \qquad\qquad \Rightarrow \underline{\underline{x = 1}} \;\; (\text{twice})$

$\qquad y = f(-\tfrac{1}{2}) = -\dfrac{27}{16} \qquad y = f(1) = 0$

$\qquad\qquad \underline{\underline{\doteqdot -1.7}}$

Table of Values :- $\qquad\qquad\qquad\qquad \{$ diagram optional $]$

x	$\rightarrow$	$-\tfrac{1}{2}$	$+\rightarrow$	$-\rightarrow$	1	$+\rightarrow$
$f'(x)$	$-$	0	$+$	$+$	0	$+$
shape	↘	→	↗	↗	→	↗

$\qquad\qquad$ Min T.P. $\qquad$ Pt of Inf

$\qquad\qquad \left(-\tfrac{1}{2}, -\tfrac{27}{16}\right) \qquad (1, 0)$

$\qquad$ or $(-0.5, -1.7)$

Minimum Turning Point at $\left(-\tfrac{1}{2}, -\tfrac{27}{16}\right)$ $\quad$ Rising Horizontal Point of Inflexion at $(1,0)$

Let $\quad y = 18 - \dfrac{1}{8}x^2 = 0 \qquad$ on the x axis

$\qquad\qquad -\dfrac{1}{8}x^2 = -18$

$\qquad\qquad\qquad x^2 = 144$

$\qquad\qquad\qquad x = \pm 12 \quad \Rightarrow \underline{\underline{A(-12, 0)}} \text{ and } \underline{\underline{B(12, 0)}}$

Q2
(b)

Area of Rectangle $= 28 \times 20 = \underline{560 \text{ ft}^2}$

Area of Parabola $= \int_{-12}^{12} \left(18 - \frac{1}{8}x^2\right) dx = 2\int_{0}^{12} \left(18 - \frac{1}{8}x^2\right) dx$

$$= 2\left[18x - \frac{x^3}{24}\right]_{0}^{12}$$

$$= 2\left(216 - \frac{1728}{24}\right)$$

$$= \underline{288 \text{ ft}^2}$$

Required Area = Area of Rectangle − Area of Parabola

$= 272 \text{ ft}^2$

$\Rightarrow$ Cost of Repainting $= 272 \times £3 = \underline{\underline{£816}}$

Q3
(a)

Eqn tangent $y = 2x + b \Rightarrow m_{\text{tangent}} = 2 \Rightarrow m_{\text{radius TC}} = \frac{-1}{2}$

Centre point C $(4, -1)$ lies on TC

$\left\{ m_t \times m_r = -1 \right\}$

Eqn TC is $y - (-1) = -\frac{1}{2}(x - 4)$

$\left\{ y - b = m(x-a) \right\}$

$2y + 2 = -x + 4$

$\underline{\underline{x + 2y = 4}}$

$\left\{ \text{"touches"} \Rightarrow \text{tangent} \right\}$

(b)

Eqn tan is $y = 2x + b \Rightarrow -2x + y = 6 \text{ Eq}①\times1 \Rightarrow -2x + y = 6 \text{ Eq}③$

Eqn rad is $x + 2y = 2 \text{ Eq}②\times2 \Rightarrow 2x + 4y = 4 \text{ Eq}④$

$③ + ④ \Rightarrow 5y = 10$

$y = 2$

The tangent meets the radius at T$(-2, 2)$

$\Rightarrow x = -2$

By the distance formula

$\Rightarrow$ T $(-2, 2)$

$Tc^2 = (4 - (-2))^2 + (-1 - 2)^2$

$\left\{ \text{use } (x-a)^2 + (y-b)^2 = r^2 \right\}$

$= 36 + 9$

$= \underline{\underline{45}}$

Hence the equation of the circle is $\underline{(x-4)^2 + (y+1)^2 = 45}$

4
a) Following the example :-

If $C = \begin{bmatrix} 3 & 4 \\ 2 & 5 \end{bmatrix}$ Then $a = 3;\ b = 4;\ c = 2;\ d = 5$

The equation is $(a-x)(d-x) - bc = 0$

$$\Rightarrow (3-x)(5-x) - 4 \times 2 = 0$$
$$15 - 8x + x^2 - 8 = 0$$
$$x^2 - 8x + 7 = 0$$
$$(x-1)(x-7) = 0$$
$$x = 1 \quad \text{OR} \quad x = 7$$

$\Rightarrow$ Eigenvalues of $C \begin{bmatrix} 3 & 4 \\ 2 & 5 \end{bmatrix}$ are 1 and 7

b) If $D = \begin{bmatrix} 3 & -1 \\ t & 1 \end{bmatrix}$ Then $a = 3;\ b = -1;\ c = t;\ d = 1$

The equation is $(3-x)(1-x) - (-1)t = 0$

$$3 - 4x + x^2 + t = 0$$
$$x^2 - 4x + t + 3 = 0$$

For equal roots $b^2 - 4ac = 0$, where $a = 1;\ b = -4;\ c = t+3$

$$(-4)^2 - 4(1)(3+t) = 0$$
$$16 - 12 - 4t = 0$$
$$-4t = -4$$
$$\underline{\underline{t = 1}}$$

$\left\{ \begin{array}{l} \text{check when } t=1 \\ x^2 - 4x + 4 = 0 \\ \Rightarrow (x-2)^2 = 0 \end{array} \right\}$

5
a) "A divides OP in the ratio 1:2" $\Rightarrow \overrightarrow{OA} : \overrightarrow{OP} = 1:3 \Rightarrow A(1,0,0)$

"B divides RP in the ratio 1:2" $\Rightarrow \overrightarrow{RB} : \overrightarrow{RP} = 1:3 \Rightarrow B(3,2,0)$

"c divides SP in the ratio 1:2" $\Rightarrow \overrightarrow{SC} : \overrightarrow{SP} = 1:3 \Rightarrow \underline{C(3,0,-2)}$

b) By the distance formula $AB^2 = (3-1)^2 + (2-0)^2 + (0-0)^2 = 8$

$$\Rightarrow AB = \sqrt{8} \qquad \{\text{OR } 2\sqrt{2}\}$$

Area $\triangle ABC = \frac{1}{2} AB \cdot AC \sin A = \frac{1}{2} \cdot \sqrt{8}\sqrt{8} \sin 60° \quad \{\text{equilateral}\}$

$$= 4 \cdot \frac{\sqrt{3}}{2}$$
$$= \underline{\underline{2\sqrt{3} \text{ units}^2}} \qquad \{\doteq 3.46 \text{ un}^2\}$$

Q5
(c)

Surface Area of Cube $= 6 \times 3 \times 3 = 54$ units^2

Area $\triangle APC = \frac{1}{2} \times 2 \times 2 = 2$ units^2 ; $\left\{ \begin{array}{l} \triangle s \; APC, \; APB \; \text{and} \; BPC \\ \text{are} \;\; \text{CONGRUENT} \\ \Rightarrow \;\; \text{EQUAL AREAS} \end{array} \right\}$

From (b) Area $\triangle ABC = 2\sqrt{3}$ units^2

Difference in Surface Areas $=$ S.A. CRYSTAL $-$ S.A. CUBE

$\qquad\qquad\qquad\qquad = \left\{ 54 - 3 \times \triangle APC + \triangle ABC \right\} - 54$

$\qquad\qquad\qquad\qquad = -3 \times \triangle APC + \triangle ABC$

$\qquad\qquad\qquad\qquad = -6 + 2\sqrt{3}$

$\qquad\qquad\qquad\qquad = 2\sqrt{3} - 6$

$\qquad\qquad\qquad\qquad \doteqdot -2.536$ units^2 $\Rightarrow$ DECREASE

$\Rightarrow$ Percentage Decrease in surface area $= \dfrac{2.536}{54} \times 100 \doteqdot 4.7\%$ decrease

---

Q6
(a)

$y = f(x) = 2 \sin 2x + 1 = 0$ on the x axis

$\qquad 2 \sin 2x \;\; = -1$

$\qquad \sin 2x \;\; = -\frac{1}{2}$

$\qquad\qquad 2x \;\; = 7\frac{\pi}{6} \; , \; 11\frac{\pi}{6} \qquad \{ \doteqdot 1.83 \; , \; 2.88 \}$

$\qquad\qquad x \;\; = 7\frac{\pi}{12} \; , \; 11\frac{\pi}{12} \quad \Rightarrow \; \dot{A}\left(7\frac{\pi}{12}, 0\right); \; B\left(11\frac{\pi}{12}, 0\right)$

(b) "ℓ" meets the graph at 3 points

(c) gradient "ℓ" $= \dfrac{0-2}{\pi - 0} = \dfrac{-2}{\pi}$

y-intersect "ℓ" $= 2$

$\Rightarrow$ Equation "ℓ" is :-

$\qquad y = -\dfrac{2}{\pi} x + 2$

3 points of intersection

C is the point $(\frac{\pi}{2}, f(\frac{\pi}{2})) \Rightarrow C(\frac{\pi}{2}, 1)$ $\qquad \left\{ \begin{array}{l} f(\frac{\pi}{2}) = 2 \sin 2 . \frac{\pi}{2} + 1 \\ = 0 + 1 \\ = 1 \end{array} \right\}$

On "ℓ" when $x = \frac{\pi}{2}$, then $y = -\dfrac{2}{\pi} . \dfrac{\pi}{2} + 2 = -1 + 2 = 1$

Hence $C(\frac{\pi}{2}, 1)$ satisfies the equation "ℓ" $\Rightarrow$ C lies ON "ℓ"

7
(a) The line (road) meets the curve (circuit) where :-

$$-4x - 3 = 5 - 2x^2 - x^3$$

$$x^3 + 2x^2 - 4x - 8 = 0$$

Factorise $f(x) = x^3 + 2x^2 - 4x - 8$

$$(x+2)(x+2)(x-2) = 0$$

```
-2 | 1    2   -4   -8
   |      -2   0    8
-2 | 1    0   -4    0  => (x+2) is factor
   |      -2   4
     1   -2    0  => (x+2) is a factor
```

$x = -2$ (twice) and $x = 2$

=> tangent at $x = -2$

where $y = 5$

=> $(x-2)$ is a factor

Hence $B(-2, 5)$ is the point of contact

$\{ f(-2) = 5 \}$

b) At $B(-2, 5)$

gradient of line $y = -4x - 3 = \underline{-4}$ $\{ y = mx + c \}$

gradient of curve $y = 5 - 2x^2 - x^3$ $\dfrac{dy}{dx} = -4x - 3x^2$ $\{ m = \dfrac{dy}{dx} \}$

At $x = -2$ $\dfrac{dy}{dx} = 8 - 12 = \underline{-4}$

Since the 2 gradients are equal, then the drivers go straight on

---

8
(a) "15% lost" => 85% remains each hour $\{ 85\% = 0.85 \}$

=> After 4 hours, the amount of serum remaining $= 0.85^4 \times 25$

$\doteqdot 13.05\,mg$

(b) After 1 dose,   Amount $\doteqdot 13.05$ mg. < 20

After 2 doses, Amount $= (13.05 + 25) \times 0.85^4 \doteqdot 19.86\,mg. < 20$

After 3 doses, Amount $= (19.86 + 25) \times 0.85^4 \doteqdot 23.42\,mg. > 20$

Hence 3 doses are needed

(c) $u_{n+1} = 0.85^4 u_n + 25$

=> $u_{n+1} = 0.522\,u_n + 25$ since $0.85^4 = 0.522$

(d) From (c) $u_{n+1} = 0.522\,u_n + 25$ => $u_1 = 25$

$u_2 = 38.05$

$u_3 = 44.86$

The level seems to approach a limit $u_4 = 48.42$

If this limit is L $u_5 = 50.27$

Then $L = 0.522L + 25$ $u_{10} = 52.2$

$0.478L = 25$

$L \doteqdot 52.3\,mg$ => No maximum length of time

$\{$ since $52.3 < 55 \}$

67

Q9
(a) Required Area "A" = Area $\triangle$ + Area of Rectangle ACDE

Area $\triangle ABC = \frac{1}{2} \times 4 \times 4 \sin\theta° = 8\sin\theta°$

Area ACDE $= \frac{1}{2}$ (Area Square ACFG)

$= \frac{1}{2} AC^2$

$= \frac{1}{2}\left(4^2 + 4^2 - 2\times 4\times 4 \cos\theta°\right)$

$= \frac{1}{2}\left(32 - 32\cos\theta°\right)$

$= \underline{16 - 16\cos\theta°}$

Hence "A" $= 8\sin\theta° + 16 - 16\cos\theta°$

$= \underline{8\left(2 + \sin\theta° - 2\cos\theta°\right)}$

$\left\{\begin{array}{l}\text{Use Cosine Rule}\\\text{to find } AC^2\end{array}\right\}$

OR ALTERNATIVELY

use

$\Rightarrow x = 4\sin\frac{\theta°}{2}$

$\Rightarrow$ Area Rectangle $= 2x^2$

Then use:-

$\sin^2\frac{\theta°}{2} = \frac{1}{2}(1 - \cos\theta°)$ etc...

(b) $8\sin\theta° - 16\cos\theta° = k\sin(\theta - \alpha)°$

$= k\sin\theta°\cos\alpha° - k\cos\theta°\sin\alpha°$

Here $\left.\begin{array}{l} k\cos\alpha° = 8 \\ k\sin\alpha° = 16 \end{array}\right\} \Rightarrow k^2 = 8^2 + 16^2 = 320$

$\Rightarrow k = \sqrt{320}$

$= 8\sqrt{5}$

$\Rightarrow \tan\alpha° = \frac{16}{8} = 2$

$\Rightarrow \alpha = 63.4$

Hence $\underline{8\sin\theta° - 16\cos\theta° = 8\sqrt{5}\sin(\theta - 63.4)°}$

(c) When "A" $= 8\sin\theta° + 16 - 16\cos\theta° = 30$ $\left\{\text{from part (a)}\right\}$

Then $16 + 8\sqrt{5}\sin(\theta - 63.4)° = 30$ $\left\{\text{from part (b)}\right\}$

$8\sqrt{5}\sin(\theta - 63.4)° = 14$

$\sin(\theta - 63.4)° \doteqdot \frac{14}{8\sqrt{5}}$ $\left\{\doteqdot 0.7826\right\}$

$\theta - 63.4 = 51.5$ $\left\{\begin{array}{l}\text{ignore } 128.5 \\ \text{as } \theta < 180\end{array}\right\}$

$\underline{\theta = 114.9}$

Q10

(a) Since the graph in figure 2 is LINEAR, Then $\log_e I = m \log_e t + C$

Here, $\underline{C = 4}$ Since $(0,4)$ is on the line

Also, $m = \dfrac{4-0}{0-5} = \dfrac{-4}{5}$ $\Rightarrow$ Eqn is $\underline{\underline{\log_e I = -\dfrac{4}{5} \log_e t + 4}}$

(b) If $I = k\,t^r$

Then $\log_e I = \log_e(k\,t^r) = \log_e t^r + \log_e k$ {Take logs Both Sides}

$\Rightarrow \log_e I = r \log_e t + \log_e k$ {compare with (a)}

From (a) $r = -\dfrac{4}{5} = \underline{-0.8}$ Also $\log_e k = 4$

$\Rightarrow k = e^4 \doteq 54.6$

Hence $\underline{\underline{I = 54.6\, t^{-0.8}}}$

Q11

(a)
$C(x) = 2x + y$

$= 2x + 100 - d$

$= 2x + 100 - \sqrt{(x^2 - 243)}$

$\Rightarrow \underline{C(x) = 2x + 100 - (x^2 - 243)^{\frac{1}{2}}}$

By Pythagoras
$x^2 = d^2 + (9\sqrt{3})^2$

$d^2 = x^2 - 243$

(diagram: right triangle P, sides $9\sqrt{3}$ km, x km, d km, y km to R, total 100 km)

(b) From (a)
$C(x) = 2x + 100 - (x^2 - 243)^{\frac{1}{2}}$

$\Rightarrow C'(x) = 2 - \dfrac{1}{2}(x^2 - 243)^{-\frac{1}{2}} \cdot (2x) = 0$ at St.Val.

$y + d = 100$
$y = 100 - d$

$\dfrac{x}{(x^2 - 243)^{\frac{1}{2}}} = 2$

$\dfrac{x^2}{x^2 - 243} = 4$

$x^2 = 4x^2 - 972$

$972 = 3x^2$

$x^2 = 324$

$\underline{\underline{x = 18}}$ {ignore $x = -18$}

$C(18) = \underline{\underline{127}}$

Hence minimum cost $= £\,127$ million

Total length $= x + y = 18 + 100 - (18^2 - 243)^{\frac{1}{2}}$

$= 118 - (81)^{\frac{1}{2}}$

$\Rightarrow \underline{\underline{\text{Total length} = 109 \text{ km}}}$ {OR 127 - 18}

Table of Values:-

x	$-$	18	$+$
$C'(x)$	$-$	0	$+$
shape	↘	→	↗

min. at $(18, 127)$

Q1
$$\int (3x^3 + 4x)\, dx = \frac{3x^4}{4} + \frac{4x^2}{2} + c$$
$$= \frac{3}{4}x^4 + 2x^2 + c$$

Q2
$$f(x) = kx^3 + 5x - 1$$
$$f'(x) = 3kx^2 + 5 \implies f'(1) = 3k + 5 = 14$$
$$3k = 9$$
$$k = 3$$

Q3
Since $ABCD$ is a parallelogram
Then $\overrightarrow{AD} = \overrightarrow{BC} \implies \underline{d} - \underline{a} = \underline{c} - \underline{b}$
$$\underline{d} = \underline{a} + \underline{c} - \underline{d}$$
$$\underline{d} = \begin{pmatrix} 2 \\ -1 \\ 4 \end{pmatrix} + \begin{pmatrix} -6 \\ 4 \\ 2 \end{pmatrix} - \begin{pmatrix} 7 \\ 1 \\ 3 \end{pmatrix}$$
$$\underline{d} = \begin{pmatrix} -11 \\ 2 \\ 3 \end{pmatrix}$$

Hence D is the point $(-11, 2, 3)$

Q4
$$\overrightarrow{RS} = \underline{s} - \underline{r} = \begin{pmatrix} 2 \\ -5 \\ 4 \end{pmatrix} - \begin{pmatrix} -1 \\ -8 \\ -2 \end{pmatrix} = \begin{pmatrix} 3 \\ 3 \\ 6 \end{pmatrix}$$

$$\overrightarrow{ST} = \underline{t} - \underline{s} = \begin{pmatrix} 3 \\ -4 \\ 6 \end{pmatrix} - \begin{pmatrix} 2 \\ -5 \\ 4 \end{pmatrix} = \begin{pmatrix} 1 \\ 1 \\ 2 \end{pmatrix}$$

Since $\overrightarrow{RS} = 3\overrightarrow{ST}$, then R, S and T are collinear

Q5
Centre $(1,1)$
$$m_{Rad.1} = \frac{2-1}{3-1} = \frac{1}{2} \implies m_{Tan.1} = -2$$

$$m_{Rad.2} = \frac{-1-1}{2-1} = -2 \implies m_{Tan.2} = \frac{1}{2}$$

Since $m_{Tan.1} \times m_{Tan.2} = -1$; Then tangents are perpendicular

Q6

$\sin\theta° + \sin(\theta+120)° + \cos(\theta+150)°$

$= \sin\theta° + \sin\theta°\cos120° + \cos\theta°\sin120° + \cos\theta°\cos150° - \sin\theta°\sin150°$

$= \sin\theta° + \sin\theta°\left(-\frac{1}{2}\right) + \cos\theta°\left(\frac{\sqrt{3}}{2}\right) + \cos\theta°\left(-\frac{\sqrt{3}}{2}\right) - \sin\theta°\left(\frac{1}{2}\right)$

$= \sin\theta° - \sin\theta° \qquad + \frac{\sqrt{3}}{2}\cos\theta° - \frac{\sqrt{3}}{2}\cos\theta°$

$= 0$

Q7

$\underline{u} + \underline{v} = \begin{pmatrix} -3 \\ 3 \\ 3 \end{pmatrix} + \begin{pmatrix} 1 \\ 5 \\ -1 \end{pmatrix} = \begin{pmatrix} -2 \\ 8 \\ 2 \end{pmatrix}$

$\underline{u} - \underline{v} = \begin{pmatrix} -3 \\ 3 \\ 3 \end{pmatrix} - \begin{pmatrix} 1 \\ 5 \\ -1 \end{pmatrix} = \begin{pmatrix} -4 \\ -2 \\ 4 \end{pmatrix}$

$(\underline{u}+\underline{v})\cdot(\underline{u}-\underline{v}) = \begin{pmatrix} -2 \\ 8 \\ 2 \end{pmatrix}\cdot\begin{pmatrix} -4 \\ -2 \\ 4 \end{pmatrix} = 8 - 16 + 8 = 0$

Since $(\underline{u}+\underline{v})\cdot(\underline{u}-\underline{v}) = 0$; then $\underline{(u+v)}$ and $(\underline{u}-\underline{v})$ are perpendicular

---

Q8
(a)

By substituting $y=x$ into $x^2+y^2-6x-2y-24 = 0$

We have $x^2+x^2-6x-2x-24 = 0$

$2x^2 - 8x - 24 = 0$

$x^2 - 4x - 12 = 0$

$(x+2)(x-6) = 0$

$x+2 = 0$ OR $x-6 = 0$

$x = -2$ $x = 6$

$y = -2$ $y = 6$ Hence $A(6,6)$

and $B(-2,-2)$

(b)

Let C be the mid point of AB

Then C, the point $(2,2)$, is the circle centre and AC is a radius

$AC^2 = (2-(-2))^2 + (2-(-2))^2 = 32$ {using the distance formula}

Hence the equation of the circle on AB is $(x-2)^2 + (y-2)^2 = 32$

$\{$or $x^2+y^2-4x-4y-24 = 0\}$

Q9 **(a)**	$u_2 = 0.9 u_1 + 2 = 0.9(3) + 2$
	Hence $u_2 = 4.7$

(b) $u_3 = 0.9 u_2 + 2$; $u_4 = 7.607$; $u_5 = 8.846$; $u_6 = 9.612$

$= 6.23$

Since $u_7 = 10.966 > 10$

Then $n = 7$ is the required value

(c) At the limit, let $u_n = u_{n-1} = u$

Then $u = 0.9u + 2$

$0.1u = 2$

$u = 20$ Hence the limit is 20

Q10
$$f(x) = \frac{1}{x^3} + \cos 3x = x^{-3} + \cos 3x$$

$$\Rightarrow f'(x) = -3x^{-4} - \sin 3x \quad (3)$$

$$f'(x) = \frac{-3}{x^4} - 3\sin 3x$$

Q11
$$x^2 + 8x + 18 = x^2 + 8x + 16 - 16 + 18$$
$$= x^2 + 8x + 16 + 2$$
$$= (x + 4)^2 + 2$$

Hence Minimum Turning Point at $(-4, 2)$

Q12 $a = 2$; $b = 1$; $c = 2$

(a) {displacement} {amplitude} {frequency}

(b) $2 + \sin 2x = 2.5$

$\sin 2x = 0.5$

$2x = \frac{\pi}{6}, \frac{5\pi}{6}$ {For $0 < x < \pi$}

$x = \frac{\pi}{12}, \frac{5\pi}{12}$

Q13

(a)

5   3   { By Pythagoras }

4

$\sin 2\theta = 2 \sin \theta \cos \theta$

$= 2 \cdot \dfrac{3}{5} \cdot \dfrac{4}{5} = \dfrac{24}{25}$

Also $\cos 2\theta = \cos^2 \theta - \sin^2 \theta$

$= \left(\dfrac{4}{5}\right)^2 - \left(\dfrac{3}{5}\right)^2 = \dfrac{7}{25}$

(b) $\sin 4\theta = 2 \sin 2\theta \cos 2\theta$

$= 2 \left(\dfrac{24}{25}\right) \cdot \left(\dfrac{7}{25}\right)$

$= \dfrac{336}{625}$

Q14

{ Gradient $= f'(x) = \tan \theta°$ }

$f(x) = 4x - x^2$

$f'(x) = 4 - 2x \implies f'(0) = 4$; Hence gradient $= 4$.

If $\tan \theta° = 4$ If $\tan d° = 1$
Then $\theta° = 75 \cdot 96$ Then $d = 45$

Required angle is $\theta - d = 30 \cdot 96$
$\doteqdot 31°$

Q15

$\cos 2x° + 5 \cos x° - 2 = 0$

$2\cos^2 x° - 1 + 5 \cos x° - 2 = 0$ { $\cos 2x° = 2\cos^2 x° - 1$ }

$2\cos^2 x° + 5 \cos x° - 3 = 0$

$(2 \cos x° - 1)(\cos x° + 3) = 0$

$2 \cos x° - 1 = 0$, or $\cos x° + 3 = 0$

$2\cos x° = 1$ $\cos x° = -3$ { No Real Roots }
$\cos x° = \frac{1}{2}$ { if $\cos x° < -1$ }

$x = 60, 300$

73

Q16

(a)

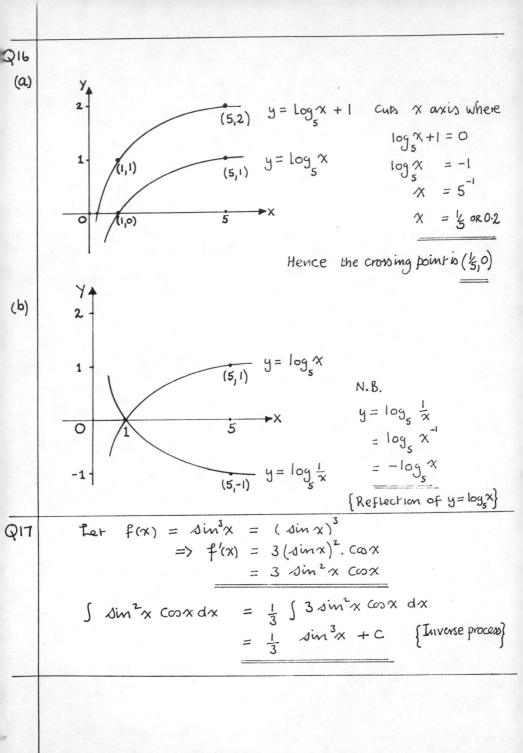

$y = \log_5 x + 1$ Cuts x axis where

$\log_5 x + 1 = 0$

$\log_5 x = -1$

$x = 5^{-1}$

$x = \frac{1}{5}$ or 0.2

Hence the crossing point is $(\frac{1}{5}, 0)$

(b)

$y = \log_5 x$

$y = \log_5 \frac{1}{x}$

N.B.

$y = \log_5 \frac{1}{x}$

$= \log_5 x^{-1}$

$= -\log_5 x$

{Reflection of $y = \log_5 x$}

Q17   Let $f(x) = \sin^3 x = (\sin x)^3$

$\Rightarrow f'(x) = 3(\sin x)^2 . \cos x$

$= 3 \sin^2 x \cos x$

$\int \sin^2 x \cos x \, dx = \frac{1}{3} \int 3 \sin^2 x \cos x \, dx$

$= \frac{1}{3} \sin^3 x + C$ {Inverse process}

74

Q18   Let S be the point $(a,0,0)$ and T be the point $(b,0,0)$

{since they both lie ON the x axis}.

$SP^2 = (a-4)^2 + (-2)^2 + (-6)^2 = 49$ {Using the distance formula}

$\qquad (a-4)^2 + 4 + 36 = 49$

$\qquad\qquad (a-4)^2 = 9$

$\qquad\qquad\quad a-4 = \pm 3$

$\qquad\qquad\quad \underline{\underline{a = 1 \text{ or } a = 7}}$

Likewise

$TP^2 = (b-4)^2 + (-2)^2 + (-6)^2 = 49$

$\qquad \Rightarrow \underline{b = 1 \text{ or } b = 7}$

Hence the points are :-

$\underline{\underline{S(1,0,0) \text{ and } T(7,0,0)}}$

Q19 $f(f(x)) = f\left(\dfrac{x}{1-x}\right) = \dfrac{\dfrac{x}{1-x}}{1 - \dfrac{x}{1-x}}$ $\left\{\text{multiply by } \dfrac{1-x}{1-x}\right\}$

$\qquad\qquad\qquad = \dfrac{x}{1-x-x}$

Hence $f(f(x)) = \dfrac{x}{1-2x}$ $\left(x \neq \frac{1}{2}\right)$

Q20   Where these graphs intersect, $3^x = 42$

$\qquad\qquad\qquad \log(3^x) = \log(42)$

$\qquad\qquad\qquad x \log 3 = \log 42$

$\qquad\qquad\qquad\quad x = \dfrac{\log 42}{\log 3}$

$\qquad\qquad\qquad\quad x = 3.4022$

$\qquad\qquad\qquad\quad \underline{x \doteqdot 3.402} \quad \{\text{To 3 d.p.}\}$

Hence the coordinates of P are $\underline{\underline{(3.402, 42)}}$

Q1
(a)

$f(x) = 2x^3 + x^2 - 13x + a$ $\qquad$ $\{$ y-intercept $= f(0) = a\}$

Since $x = 2$ is a Root then $f(2) = 0$

(b)

$$
\begin{array}{r|rrrr}
2 & 2 & 1 & -13 & a \\
  &   & 4 & 10 & -6 \\
-3 & 2 & 5 & -3 & 0 \\
  &   & -6 & 3 & \\
\hline
  & 2 & -1 & 0 &
\end{array}
$$

$\Rightarrow a - 6 = 0$

$\underline{a = 6} \Rightarrow$ point $(0, 6)$

$\Rightarrow (x+3)$ is a factor

$\underline{x = -3 \text{ is a Root}}$

$\Rightarrow (2x - 1)$ is a factor

$x = \frac{1}{2}$ is a Root

Hence other points are $\underline{\underline{(-3, 0) \text{ and } (\frac{1}{2}, 0)}}$

Q2
(a)

$m_{OD} = \frac{1}{2}$ $\Rightarrow$ $m_{AD} = -2$ $\qquad$ $\{ m_1 \times m_2 = -1 \}$

Equation $_{AD}$ $\begin{cases} \text{Point } A(3, 4) & \{\text{use } y - b = m(x-a)\} \\ & y - 4 = -2(x - 3) \\ \text{Gradient} = -2 & \underline{y = -2x + 10} \end{cases}$

(b)

At D, $y = \frac{1}{2}x$ $\qquad$ $\{$ Simultaneous equations $\}$

and $\underline{y = -2x + 10}$

Hence $0 = 2\frac{1}{2}x - 10$

$x = 4$

By substitution $y = 2$ $\left.\right\} \Rightarrow \underline{\underline{D \text{ is the point } (4, 2)}}$

(c)

Area $ABCD = AD^2 = (4-3)^2 + (2-4)^2$ $\qquad$ $\{$ Distance formula $\}$

$\Rightarrow \underline{\underline{\text{Area} = 5 \text{ units}^2}}$

Q3
(a) $B(6,4,2)$; $C(4,3,4)$; $D(6,2,2)$

(b) Mid point of $AD = \left(\dfrac{2+6}{2}, \dfrac{4+2}{2}, \dfrac{6+2}{2}\right)$

$= (4, 3, 4) = C$

(c) $\vec{OA} = \underline{a} = \begin{pmatrix} 2 \\ 4 \\ 6 \end{pmatrix} \Rightarrow |\underline{a}| = \sqrt{(2^2+4^2+6^2)} = \sqrt{56}$

$\vec{OB} = \underline{b} = \begin{pmatrix} 6 \\ 4 \\ 2 \end{pmatrix} \Rightarrow |\underline{b}| = \sqrt{(6^2+4^2+2^2)} = \sqrt{56}$

$\cos A\hat{O}B = \dfrac{\underline{a}\cdot\underline{b}}{|\underline{a}||\underline{b}|} = \dfrac{\begin{pmatrix}2\\4\\6\end{pmatrix}\cdot\begin{pmatrix}6\\4\\2\end{pmatrix}}{\sqrt{56}\ \sqrt{56}} = \dfrac{12+16+12}{56} = \dfrac{40}{56}$

$\Rightarrow A\hat{O}B = 44.4°$

(d) Since $OA = OB = \sqrt{56}$

Then $\triangle ABO$ is isosceles $\Rightarrow 2A° + 44.4° = 180°$

$2A° = 135.6°$

Hence angle $OAB = 67.8°$

Q4
(a)
(i) From the equations of the circles :-

Centre of small wheel is $(0,3)$
Centre of large wheel is $(14,10)$ } Distance$^2 = 14^2+7^2$

$= 245$

$\Rightarrow$ Distance $= \sqrt{(245)}$

$\doteqdot 15.65$ units

As 1 unit $= 5$cm ; then Distance $\doteqdot 78.3$ cm

(ii) Radius$_{small} = \sqrt{(0+9-0)} = 3$

Radius$_{large} = \sqrt{(14^2+10^2-196)} = 10$ } Sum of Radii $= 13$ units $= 65$ cm

Hence the clearance is $78.3 - 65 = 13.3$cm

$= 133$ mm

Q4
(b)
(i)
(ii)

$B(7,3)$ $P(14,10)$ $\Rightarrow$ $m_{BP} = \dfrac{10-3}{14-7} = 1 =$

Since BP bisects AC, then   BP is perpendicular to AC

Hence $m_{AC} = -1$ $\{ m_1 \times m_2 = -1 \}$

Equation_{AC} $\begin{cases} B(7,3) \\ \\ m = -1 \end{cases}$ $\begin{aligned} & y - 3 = -1(x-7) \\ & \underline{\underline{y = -x + 10}} \end{aligned}$

Eqn Chord $y = -x + 10$ $\begin{cases} y^2 = x^2 - 20x + 100 \\ -20y = 20x - 200 \end{cases}$

Eqn Circle $x^2 + y^2 - 28x - 20y + 196 = 0$

By Substitution :-

$$x^2 + x^2 - 20x + 100 - 28x + 20x - 200 + 196 = 0$$

$$2x^2 - 28x + 96 = 0$$

$$x^2 - 14x + 48 = 0$$

$$(x - 8)(x - 6) = 0$$

$$x = 8 \qquad \text{OR} \qquad x = 6$$

$$\underline{y = 2} \qquad\qquad\qquad \underline{y = 4}$$

Hence $\underline{A(8,2) \text{ and } C(6,4)}$

Q5
(a)

$f(x) = 3\sin x° - \cos x° = k \sin(x - \alpha)°$

$\qquad\qquad 3\sin x° - \cos x° = k \sin x° \cos \alpha° - k \cos x° \sin \alpha°$

Hence $\left. \begin{array}{l} -k \sin \alpha° = -1 \\ k \cos \alpha° = 3 \end{array} \right\}$ $\Rightarrow -\tan \alpha° = \dfrac{-1}{3}$

$\qquad\qquad\qquad\qquad\qquad\qquad\qquad \underline{\underline{\alpha = 18.4}}$

Also $k^2 = (-1)^2 + 3^2 = 10$

$\qquad\qquad k = \sqrt{10}$

Hence $f(x) = 3\sin x° - \cos x° = \underline{\sqrt{10} \sin(x - 18.4)°}$

Q5

(b)

$$3 \sin x° - \cos x° = \sqrt{5}$$

$$\Rightarrow \sqrt{10} \sin (x - 18.4)° = \sqrt{5} \qquad \{ \text{From part (a)} \}$$

$$\sin (x - 18.4)° = \frac{\sqrt{5}}{\sqrt{10}}$$

$$\sin (x - 18.4)° = 0.707$$

$$x - 18.4 = 45, 135$$

$$x = 63.4, 153.4$$

(c)

$$3 \sin x° - \cos x° = \sqrt{10} \sin (x - 18.4)° \leq \sqrt{5} \quad \text{where :-}$$

$$0 \leq x \leq 63.4 \quad \text{AND} \quad 153.4 \leq x \leq 180$$

$\{$ max. Val. of $f(x)$ at $x = 108.4$ $\}$
At $x = 108.4$, $f(x)$ is $\sqrt{10}$

Q6

(a)

$$f(x) = 2x^3 + 3x - 1$$

$$f(0) = -1$$
$$f(0.5) = 0.75$$ $\}$ Change of sign $\Rightarrow$ Root in the interval

$$0 < x < 0.5$$

(b)

$$2x^3 + 3x = 1$$

$$x(2x^2 + 3) = 1$$

Recurrence Relation

$$x = \frac{1}{2x^2 + 3} \quad \Rightarrow \quad x_{n+1} = \frac{1}{2x_n^2 + 3}$$

$$x_1 = 0.25$$
$$x_2 = 0.32$$
$$x_3 = 0.312$$
$$x_4 = 0.313$$
$$x_5 = 0.313$$ $\}$ agree to 3 d.p.

Hence the required root is $x = 0.31$ to 2 d.p.

Q7
(a)

Area $\triangle AEF$ = Area Rectangle $ABCD$ − (Areas of $\triangle s$ $ABE + ADF + ECF$)

$$= \quad 8 \times 6 \quad - \left(\tfrac{1}{2} \times 8x + \tfrac{1}{2}(8-x)6 + \tfrac{1}{2}(6-x)x\right)$$

$$= \quad 48 \quad - \left(4x + 24 - 3x + 3x - \tfrac{x^2}{2}\right)$$

$$\Rightarrow H(x) = \quad 24 - 4x + \frac{x^2}{2}$$

(b)

$$H(x) = \frac{x^2}{2} - 4x + 24$$

$$H'(x) = x - 4 = 0 \text{ at St. Val.}$$

$$x = 4$$
$$y = 16$$

x	→	4	→
$H'(x)$	−	0	+
Shape	↘	→	↗

min T.P.
at $(4, 16)$

Also, if $x = 0$
then $H(0) = 24$
This is the maximum Area

Hence Least Area = 16 units^2
Greatest Area = 24 units^2

Q8
(a)

$$f(x) = 4x^2 - 3x + 5$$

$$\Rightarrow f(x+1) = 4(x+1)^2 - 3(x+1) + 5$$
$$= 4(x^2 + 2x + 1) - 3x - 3 + 5$$
$$= 4x^2 + 5x + 6$$

$$f(x-1) = 4(x-1)^2 - 3(x-1) + 5$$
$$= 4(x^2 - 2x + 1) - 3x + 3 + 5$$
$$= 4x^2 - 11x + 12$$

$$\frac{f(x+1) - f(x-1)}{2} = \frac{4x^2 + 5x + 6 - (4x^2 - 11x + 12)}{2}$$

$$= \frac{16x - 6}{2}$$

$$= 8x - 3$$

Q8
(b)

$$g(x) = 2x^2 + 7x - 8$$

$$g(x+1) = 2(x+1)^2 + 7(x+1) - 8$$

$$= 2(x^2 + 2x + 1) + 7x + 7 - 8 = 2x^2 + 11x + 1$$

$$g(x-1) = 2(x-1)^2 + 7(x-1) - 8$$

$$= 2(x^2 - 2x + 1) + 7x - 7 - 8 = 2x^2 + 3x - 13$$

Hence $\dfrac{g(x+1) - g(x-1)}{2} = \dfrac{2x^2 + 11x + 1 - (2x^2 + 3x - 13)}{2}$

$$= \frac{8x + 14}{2}$$

$$= \underline{\underline{4x + 7}}$$

(c)

$$f(x) = 4x^2 - 3x + 5 ; \quad \frac{f(x+1) - f(x-1)}{2} = 8x - 3 ; \quad \left\{ f'(x) = 8x - 3 \right\}$$

$$g(x) = 2x^2 + 7x - 8 ; \quad \frac{g(x+1) - g(x-1)}{2} = 4x + 7 ; \quad \left\{ g'(x) = 4x + 7 \right\}$$

If $h(x) = 3x^2 + 5x - 1$

Then $\dfrac{h(x+1) - h(x-1)}{2} = \underline{\underline{6x + 5}}$ as this is $h'(x)$

Q9

$$y = x^2 + px + q$$

(a) At $A(2,2)$; $2 = 2^2 + 2p + q$

$$-2 = 2p + q$$

$$\underline{\underline{q = -2p - 2}} \quad \text{OR} \quad \underline{\underline{p = -\tfrac{1}{2}(q+2)}}$$

(b)

$$f(x) = x^2 + px + q$$

$$f'(x) = 2x + p \quad = \text{gradient of the curve}$$

$$f'(2) = 4 + p \quad = \quad 1 \qquad \{\text{gradient of tangent at } A\}$$

$$\left. \begin{array}{l} p = -3 \\ q = 4 \end{array} \right\} \text{Hence Eqn is } \underline{\underline{y = x^2 - 3x + 4}}$$

(c) for $y = x^2 - 3x + 4$; $\left. \begin{array}{l} a=1 \\ b=-3 \\ c=4 \end{array} \right\} \Rightarrow b^2 - 4ac = 9 - 4 \times 1 \times 4 = -7$, No Real Roots

Curve doesn't meet the x axis

Q10

At $y = 1$; $\frac{1}{4} x^2 = 1$

$x^2 = 4$

$\underline{x = \pm 2}$

At $y = 9$; $\frac{1}{4} x^2 = 9$

$x^2 = 36$

$\underline{x = \pm 6}$

This area is symmetrical about the y axis.

Area in the first quadrant can be split up as shown:-

$\text{Area} = 8 \times 2 + 9 \times 4 - \int_{2}^{6} \frac{1}{4} x^2 dx$

$= 52 - \left[\frac{x^3}{12} \right]_{2}^{6}$

$= 52 - \left\{ \left(\frac{6^3}{12} \right) - \left(\frac{2^3}{12} \right) \right\}$

$= 52 - \left\{ 18 - \frac{2}{3} \right\}$

$= 52 - 17\frac{1}{3}$

$= \underline{\frac{104}{3}}$

{ Other divisions of the area are possible }

$\Rightarrow$ Required Area = $\underline{\frac{208}{3}} \, m^2$ { Multiply by 2 }

$\Rightarrow$ Required Volume = $\underline{\underline{4160 \, m^3}}$ { Multiply by 60 }

N.B. Another solution to Q10, involves integration w.r. to "y"

If $y = \frac{1}{4} x^2$ Then $x = 2\sqrt{y}$

$= 2y^{1/2}$

$\text{Area} = 2 \int_{1}^{9} (2y^{1/2}) dy$

$= 2 \left[\frac{4}{3} y^{3/2} \right]_{1}^{9}$

$= 2 \left\{ \left(\frac{4}{3} \cdot 9^{3/2} \right) - \left(\frac{4}{3} \cdot 1^{3/2} \right) \right\}$

$= 2 \left(36 - \frac{4}{3} \right)$

$= \underline{69\frac{1}{3} \, m^2} \Rightarrow \text{Vol} = \underline{\underline{4160 \, m^3}}$

$y = \frac{1}{4} x^2$

OR

$x = 2\sqrt{y}$

GRAPHICS CALCULATOR

Using a graphics calculator can help you in understanding mathematics and can also be of assistance in sitting Higher Mathematics.

However, the S.E.B. stipulates in the Instructions to Candidates that:

1. Full credit will be given only where the solution contains appropriate working.

2. Calculators may be used.

3. Answers obtained by readings from scale drawings will **not** receive any credit.

Furthermore, the S.E.B. also states that:

Any diagram which is one of
- a scale drawing
- a coordinate diagram on a grid drawn on plain paper
- the display of a graphics calculator

and used as the **sole means** of solving a question will be considered as a 'scale drawing' under Instruction **3** of the rubric.

ILLUSTRATIVE EXAMPLES

Instruction 1

Solve the equation $3 \sin \frac{1}{2} x° - 1 = 0$ for $0 \leqslant x \leqslant 180$.

- The answer $x = 38.9$, without any appropriate working, would receive **no** credit.
- Candidates who choose to solve this equation graphically, by means of a graphics calculator for example, would need to indicate that they drew the graph of, a sketch (from the screen) where they would find the solution(s) and how they came about the answer '38.9'.

Instances of appropriate working:

A 'standard' solution

$$3 \sin \frac{1}{2} x° - 1 = 0$$
$$\frac{1}{2} x = \sin^{-1} \frac{1}{3}$$
$$= 19.47, \ (160.53 \ \ldots \ldots)$$
$$x = 38.94$$
$$x = 38.9$$

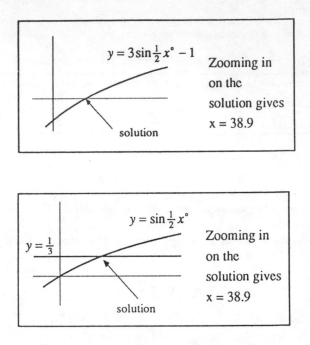

If the candidate is asked to find the stationary point(s) of functions other than quadratic or trigonometric functions, then differentiation is the only acceptable strategy.

If the candidate is asked to 'justify' the nature of the stationary point(s), then differentiation is the only acceptable strategy.

Solve algebraically $3 \sin 2x° = 2 \sin x°$ for $0 \leqslant x \leqslant 360$.

- Candidates can expect to have to produce a solution by making use of the double-angle formula and the word 'algebraically' will be used to indicate that it would be incorrect for a candidate to solve the equation by a graphical method.

Instruction 2

In and after the 1993 examination, books of mathematical tables will no longer be issued to candidates and candidates will not be permitted to bring their own books of tables into the examination room. The regulations with regard to calculators are as specified in the relevant paragraph of the Board's annually published booklet entitled "Conditions and Arrangements".

Instruction 3

The following question could be solved by an accurate coordinate diagram.

"In the diagram, A is the point (7, 0), B is (−3, −2) and C is (−1, 8).

The median CE and the altitude BD intersect at J.

(a) Find the equation of CE and BD.

(b) Find the coordinates of J.

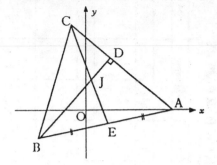

- Such a solution from an accurate coordinate diagram would receive **no** credit.

- Also, under Instruction 1, any solution, without appropriate working would receive **no** credit.

N.B.

As the illustrative examples printed here are only a selection of those given in the notes issued by the S.E.B., candidates are advised to consult the actual notes to clarify the amendments to rubric of Papers I & II as issued by the S.E.B. You should be able to obtain a complete set of these notes from your teacher.

QUESTION FREQUENCY CHART FOR REVISED HIGHER PAPERS

Topic	1989 Paper		1990 Paper		1991 Paper		1992 Paper		1993 Paper		1994 Paper	
	I	II	I	II	I	II	I	II	I	II	I	II
The Straight Line	1		20	2	1,2	1,10	2		2,10			2
Differentiation 1 Basics, Max, Min, Graph	12,13,14	1,7	2,11,16	1	5		1,19	1,5	4	1,7	2,14	7
Quadratic Theory	8		18		18		17		3		11	9
Trigonometry Reminders and Radians	11		10,15	10		3a		8	17		12	
Sequences		6		3	11	9		3		8	9	6
Functions and Graphs	19	4	6	6a.c	9,14,15,19		6,10		8,13,14		19	
Compound Angle Formulae (trig.)	7,15		9		12,20	3b	5,13	7	6,19a	6	6,13,15	
Differentiation 2 Trig. & Chain Rule	10		19		13		11		9,21	11	10,17	
The Circle	18	5	3,7	8	8	2	9,16	9	5,18	3	5,8	4
Polynomials Remainder Theorem	2	3	1	6b	6		3		7			1
Integration	5,16	1d,10	8,13	7	10,16	11	4,8,14	10a,b	11,19b	2	1	10
Vectors	3,4,6,9	2	4,5,12	4	3,7,17	5	15,18	2	1,16	5	3,4,7,18	3
The Wave Function		9		5		8	7	10c		9		5
Exponential and Log Functions	17,20,21		14,17		4	4,7	12	4	15,20	10	16,20	
Miscellaneous Questions		8		9		6		6		4		8

NOTES

NOTES

Printed by Bell and Bain Ltd., Glasgow